Problems on
QUANTITATIVE
GENETICS

Problems on
QUANTITATIVE
GENETICS

D. S. Falconer

Department of Genetics and
University of Edinburgh

Longman
London and New York

Newport

Longman Group Limited
Longman House, Burnt Mill, Harlow
Essex CM20 2JE, UK
Associated companies throughout the world

*Published in the United States of America
by Longman Inc., New York*

© Longman Group Limited 1983

First published 1983

British Library Cataloguing in Publication Data

Falconer, D. S.
　Problems on quantitative genetics.
　1. Population – genetics
　I. Title
　575.1′5　　QH455

　ISBN 0-582-44679-1

Library of Congress Cataloging in Publication Data
Falconer, D. S. (Douglas Scott)
　Problems on quantitative genetics.

　'Prepared specifically for use with Introduction to quantitative genetics (2nd edition)' – Pref.
　1. Quantitative genetics – Problems, exercises, etc. I. Falconer, D. S. (Douglas Scott. Introduction to quantitative genetics. 2nd ed. II. Title.
　QH452.7.F344　1983　575.1　82-4695

Set in 10/12 pt Monophoto Times New Roman
Printed in Hong Kong by
Astros Printing Ltd

CONTENTS

PREFACE

These problems have been prepared specifically for use with *Introduction to Quantitative Genetics* (2nd edn). Though most of the problems will be intelligible without reference to the book, many of the solutions will not be easy to follow without it because frequent reference is made to the numbered equations and occasionally to some of the Figures. The problems are arranged in order of the chapters in the book, and there is a problem on all the main points in each chapter. Some of the problems are based on the data and solutions of earlier problems. Students are therefore advised to keep their working and solutions for later use; this will save the repetition of calculations. The problems are of varied difficulty, the more difficult ones being mainly toward the end of each chapter. I hope that all students will find some that they can solve immediately and some also that will tax their ingenuity to the full.

When problems are based on imaginary data the arithmetic can be made easy but the exercise tends to be dull. So I have based the problems on real data wherever I could in order to make them more interesting and more realistic. In consequence, however, the arithmetic seldom works out simply and a pocket calculator will be needed for most of the problems.

The solutions given contain fairly full explanations of how the problems are solved and give all the main steps in the calculations. Standard statistical procedures, however, are not fully explained. The statistical calculations required are χ^2 tests of 'goodness of fit'; mean, variance and standard error of the mean; correlation and regression coefficients; analysis of variance. I have tried to ensure that there are no rounding errors in the solutions, and the steps in the calculations are given with as many decimal places as are needed for this purpose. Sampling errors in the data have for the most part been ignored and the solutions are sometimes given with more precision than is justified by the data.

I am very greatly indebted to Dr W. G. Hill for many suggestions about the problems and their solutions; his advice has been invaluable. I am very grateful also to Dr Paul M. Sharp for many helpful suggestions and for checking all the solutions; to Professor N. W. Simmonds for comments on the problems concerning plants; and to many other colleagues for suggestions, particularly about sources of suitable data. The responsibility for any errors that remain is

mine alone. I should be greatful to readers if they will tell me of any errors that
they find.

Institute of Animal Genetics
West Mains Road
Edinburgh EH9 3JN
Scotland

D. S. Falconer
April, 1982

I GENETIC CONSTITUTION OF A POPULATION

M₁ **1.1** The following numbers of the human M-N blood groups were recorded in a sample of American Whites.

M	MN	N
1787	3039	1303

(1) What are the genotype frequencies observed in this sample?
(2) What are the gene frequencies?
(3) With the gene frequencies observed, what are the genotype frequencies expected from the Hardy–Weinberg law?
(4) How well do the observed frequencies agree with the expectation?

Data from Wiener, A. S. (1943) quoted by Stern, C. (1973) *Principles of Human Genetics*. Freeman, San Francisco.

[Solution 1]

Ma **1.2** About 30 per cent of people do not recognize the bitter taste of phenyl-thio-carbamate (PTC). Inability to taste it is due to a single autosomal recessive gene. What is the frequency of the non-tasting gene, assuming the population to be in Hardy–Weinberg equilibrium?

[Solution 11]

Me **1.3** Albinism occurs with a frequency of about 1 in 20,000 in European populations. Assuming it to be due to a single autosomal recessive gene, and assuming the population to be in Hardy–Weinberg equilibrium, what proportion of people are carriers? Only an approximate answer is needed.

[Solution 21]

Mm **1.4** As an exercise in algebra, work out the gene frequency of a recessive mutant in a random-breeding population that would result in one third of normal individuals being carriers.

[Solution 31]

Ma **1.5** Three allelic variants, A, B, and C, of the red cell acid phosphatase

I

enzyme were found in a sample of 178 English people. All genotypes are distinguishable by electrophoresis, and the frequencies in the sample were

Genotype	AA	AB	BB	AC	BC	CC
Frequency (%)	9.6	48.3	34.3	2.8	5.0	0.0

What are the gene frequencies in the sample? Why were no CC individuals
found?

Data from Spencer, N., *et al.* (1964) *Nature*, **201**, 299–300.

[Solution 41]

1.6   About 7 per cent of men are colour-blind in consequence of a sex-
linked recessive gene. Assuming Hardy–Weinberg equilibrium, what proportion
of women are expected to be (1) carriers, and (2) colour-blind? (3) In what
proportion of marriages are both husband and wife expected to be colour-
blind?

[Solution 51]

1.7   Sine oculis (*so*) and cinnabar (*cn*) are two autosomal recessive genes
in *Drosophila melanogaster*. They are very closely linked and can be treated as if
they were alleles at one locus. The 'heterozygote', *so/cn*, is wild-type and is
distinguishable from both homozygotes; (*so/so* has no eyes; *cn/cn* has white
eyes if the stock is made homozygous for another eye-colour mutant, brown,
bw). In a class experiment 4 males and 4 females of an *so/so* stock were put in a
vial together with 16 males and 16 females from a *cn/cn* stock and allowed to
mate. There were 20 such vials. The total count of progeny, classified by genotype, was as follows.

so/so	*so/cn*	*cn/cn*
135	359	947

How do these numbers differ from the Hardy–Weinberg expectations? Suggest
a reason for the discrepancy.

[Solution 61]

1.8   Suppose that *Drosphila* cultures are set up in vials as described in
Problem 1.7, but this time with a gene frequency of 0.5. This is done by putting
10 males and 10 females of each stock in each vial. The supply of *so/so* females
ran out and only 4 were left for the last vial. So, to preserve the intended gene
frequency and numbers of parents, this vial was made up as follows: 16♂♂+4♀♀
of *so/so* with 4♂♂+16♀♀ of *cn/cn*. The student who got this vial was a bit
surprised by what he found. What genotype frequencies would you expect in the
progeny?

[Solution 71]

1.9   Prove that when there are any number of alleles at a locus the total frequency of heterozygotes is greatest when all alleles have the same frequency. What is then the total frequency of heterozygotes?

[Solution 81]

Mi   **1.10**   Suppose that a strain of genotype AA BB is mixed with another strain of genotype aa bb, with equal numbers of the two strains and equal numbers of males and females, which mate at random. Call this generation of parents and their progeny generation 0. Subsequent generations also mate at random and there are no differences of fertility or viability among the genotypes. What will be the frequency of the genotype AA bb in the generation 2 progeny if the two loci are (1) unlinked, (2) linked with a recombination frequency of 20 per cent?

[Solution 91]

Ma   **1.11**   How will the solutions of Problem 1.10 be altered if the two strains are crossed by taking males of one strain and females of the other?

[Solution 101]

> gamete – gamete = a generation

2 CHANGES OF GENE FREQUENCY

2.1 Rare white-flowered plants occur in populations of a *Delphinium* species which normally has deep blue flowers. In an area in the Rocky Mountains the frequency of white-flowered plants was 7.4×10^{-4}. White-flowered plants were found to set an average of 143 seeds per plant while blue-flowered plants set 229, the reduction in seed-production being due to discrimination by pollinators, which are bumblebees and humming birds. On the assumption that white flowers are due to a single recessive gene, and that the population was in equilibrium, what rate of mutation would be needed to balance the selection?

Data from Waser, N. M. & Price, M. V. (1981) *Evolution*, **35**, 376–90.

[Solution 12]

2.2 If the white flowers in Problem 2.1 were due to a completely dominant gene, which is less likely, what would be the mutation rate needed to maintain equilibrium?

[Solution 22]

2.3 If an allele, *A*, mutates to *a* with a frequency of 1 in 10,000 and back-mutates with a frequency 1 in 100,000, and if the three genotypes have equal fitnesses, what will be the genotype frequencies at equilibrium in a random-mating population?

[Solution 32]

2.4 Refer to Problem 2.3. What would be the consequences of doubling the mutation rate in both directions?

[Solution 42]

2.5 Medical treatment is, or will be, available for several serious auto-somal recessive diseases. What would be the long-term consequences if treatment allowed sufferers from such a disease to have on average half the number of children that normal people have, whereas without treatment they would have no children? Assume that the present frequency is the mutation versus selection

4

equilibrium, that in the longterm a new equilibrium will be reached, and that no other circumstances change.

[Solution 52]

2.6 Cystic fibrosis is an autosomal recessive human disease with an incidence of about 1 in 2,500 live births among Caucasians. What would be the consequence in the immediately following generation if the mutation rate were doubled? Assume that the present frequency is the mutation versus selection equilibrium, that back-mutation is negligible, and that affected individuals have no children. Express your result as a percentage increase of incidence and as the number of additional cases per million births.

[Solution 62]

2.7 A careless *Drosophila* stock-keeper allows a stock of a dominant autosomal mutant to be contaminated by wild-type flies. Originally all flies were homozygous for the mutant, but after 10 generations some wild-type flies were found in the stock. Precautions were then taken to prevent further contamination. Suppose that we make the following assumptions: (i) In every generation 1 per cent of flies were contaminants, (ii) all contaminants were homozygous wild-type, (iii) mutant and wild-type flies have equal fitness. With these assumptions what would be (1) the proportion of wild-type flies in the generations after the last contamination, and (2) the proportion of heterozygotes among the flies with the mutant phenotype?

[Solution 72]

2.8 The two closely linked recessive genes of *Drosophila* described in Problem 1.7 can be treated as alleles. Two populations were set up with initial gene frequencies of *so* of 0.2 in one and 0.8 in the other. After 7 generations of random breeding the gene frequency of *so* was close to 0.35 in both populations. What does this tell us about the selection operating?

[Solution 82]

2.9 The gene that makes wild rats resistant to the anticoagulant poison warfarin exhibits heterozygote advantage because rats homozygous for the resistance gene suffer from vitamin K deficiency. Heterozygotes are resistant to the poison and do not suffer from vitamin K deficiency. The proportion of resistant homozygotes that die from vitamin K deficiency was estimated to be 63 per cent. Susceptible homozygotes are not all killed when poison is applied to an area. A population under continuous treatment with poison came to equilibrium with the resistance gene at a frequency of 0.34. What percentage of all rats in this population will die in consequence of the resistance gene and the poisoning.

Data from Greaves, J. H., *et al.* (1977) *Genet. Res.* **30**, 257–63.

[Solution 92]

2.10   Suppose that two mutant genes are used in a class experiment on selection in *Drosophila*. In both cases heterozygotes are distinguishable from homozygotes but the genes are recessive with respect to fitness. (These are not known genes.) With gene (a) mutant homozygotes of both sexes have their fertility reduced by 50 per cent relative to the other genotypes, but have un-impaired viability. With gene (b) mutant homozygotes are fully fertile but both sexes have their pre-adult mortality increased by 50 per cent relative to the other genotypes. In both cases a parental population is made up of $30\male\male + 30\female\female$ homozygous wild-type and $20\male\male + 20\female\female$ homozygous mutant. What genotype frequencies will be found in the progeny? How do they compare with Hardy–Weinberg expectations based on the observed gene frequency in the <u>progeny</u>? What conclusions about the selection can be drawn from the frequencies in the progeny? Why does Δq differ in the two cases?

[Solution 102]

2.11   Derive an expression for the change of gene frequency, Δq, resulting from one generation of selection against a sex-linked recessive lethal gene. Assume that the population before selection has Hardy–Weinberg genotype frequencies and equal gene frequencies in males and females.

[Solution 112]

2.12   What is the approximate equilibrium gene frequency of a deleterious sex-linked recessive gene, when selection is balanced by a mutation rate of u? Human X-linked muscular dystrophy was found in a survey in England to have an incidence of 32.6 per 100,000 males. The mutation rate was estimated from the number of 'sporadic' cases to be 10.5×10^{-5}. Do these estimates agree with the expectation for a population in equilibrium when sufferers from the disease do not reproduce and carriers have normal survival and fertility?

Data from Gardner–Medwin, D. (1970) *J. Med. Genet.*, **7**, 334–7.

[Solution 122]

2.13   Red coat colour in many breeds of cattle is due to an autosomal recessive gene, the dominant phenotype being black. Suppose that 1 per cent of red calves are born in a predominantly black breed, and suppose that it is desired to eliminate the red gene. Assuming the genotypes in the initial population to be in Hardy–Weinberg proportions, what proportion of red calves would there be after applying the following alternative selection procedures over two generations? (1) No red animals are used for breeding. (2) In addition to culling all red animals, all black bulls to be used for breeding are first tested by 6 progeny each from cows known to be heterozygotes. Any bull producing one or more red calves in the test is discarded. Cows used for breeding are not tested.

[Solution 132]

3 SMALL POPULATIONS:
I. Changes of gene frequency under simplified conditions

In working the problems on Chapter 3, treat the populations as if they were idealized populations.

3.1 Cod fish have two forms of haemoglobin determined by alleles *a* and *b* at one locus. A sample of cod taken off the Norwegian coast had the following frequencies of the three genotypes.

aa	ab	bb	Total
130	763	1698	2591

f(homo) > expected

Are these frequencies compatible with the sample having been drawn from a random-breeding population? What do they suggest about the breeding structure of the population?   asst mtg, wahlund effect,

Data from Møller, D. (1968) *Hereditas*, **60**, 1–32.

[Solution 3]

3.2 Among the cod described in Problem 3.1 two distinct races can be recognized by anatomical differences in the otoliths. When the sample was separated into the two races, called 'Arctic' and 'Coastal', the following numbers were found.

	aa	ab	bb	Total
Arctic	23	250	946	1219
Coastal	107	513	752	1372

asst mtg between. HW within

What further light does this throw on the question in Problem 3.1?

[Solution 13]

3.3 If a population is maintained by random mating among 20 pairs of parents in every generation, what will be its inbreeding coefficient after 5 and after 10 generations?   .12   .06

[Solution 23]

x 3.5

3.4 Suppose that for a class experiment each student was given 10 pairs

7

of unmated *Drosophila* taken at random from a large stock in which an electrophoretic variant was present at a gene frequency of 0.3. Each student then maintained his sub-population by taking 10 pairs at random to be parents of the next generation. After 5 generations each student determined the gene frequency in his own population by electrophoresis of a sample of 20 flies from the progeny. What would be the average gene frequency found? How much variation would you expect to find among the students in their estimated gene frequencies, assuming that all read their gels correctly?

[Solution 33]

3.5   If the numbers of the three genotypes counted by the students in the experiment of Problem 3.4 were put together, what would be the overall frequencies of the genotypes?

[Solution 43]

3.6   A stock of mice consisted of 18 lines all derived from the same base population but bred separately thereafter. The stock was polymorphic for an autosomal enzyme locus, *Got-1*, with two alleles, *a* and *b*. After 27 generations mice from all the lines were typed by electrophoresis for the genotypes at this locus and the following numbers were found.

aa	*ab*	*bb*	Total
42	76	448	566

What is the inbreeding coefficient indicated by these numbers?

Data from Garnett, I. (1973) *Ph.D. Thesis*. University of Edinburgh.

[Solution 53]

3.7   Suppose that a random-breeding population is sampled and the following genotype frequencies of a protein variant are found.

aa	*ab*	*bb*
0.34	0.52	0.14

(1) Ignoring the question of significance, do these frequencies give evidence of some form of selection operating on the genotypes? (2) How would the conclusion be altered by the knowledge that the individuals in the sample were the progeny of 4 pairs of parents?

[Solution 63]

3.8   Modify equation [3.16] so as to be applicable when there are different numbers of male and female parents, as is usually the case with domestic livestock.

[Solution 73]

4 SMALL POPULATIONS: II. Less simplified conditions

Mi

4.1 Suppose that four *Drosophila* stocks are maintained by putting a fixed number of unmated adults in a bottle and allowing them to mate at random. All stocks have 10 female parents but different numbers of male parents, the numbers of males being 10, 5, 2 and 1 respectively. Calculate the effective population size of each stock and the inbreeding coefficient after 10 generations. Assume that there are no differences of fertility among females or among males.

$N_e = 15 \quad 13.3 \quad 6.6 \quad 3.6$

$F_t = .22 - .31 , .5 - .7$

[Solution 83]

Mo

4.2 The sex ratio among breeding individuals can be expressed as the number of females per male. Modify equation [4.4] so as to express N_e in terms of the number of females, N_f, and the number of females per male, d.

$\dfrac{4N_f}{1+d}$

[Solution 93]

Muy

4.3 Suppose that an isolated natural population goes through a regular 5-year cycle of numbers, with the numbers of breeding pairs in successive generations being 500, 50, 100, 200, 400. What is the effective population size and the rate of inbreeding?

[Solution 103]

Me

4.4 Compare the (approximate) rates of inbreeding in two varieties of a plant, one of which is self-fertile and the other self-sterile, when both are propagated by random pollination among 20 individual plants.

[Solution 113]

Mt

4.5 It is planned to keep a mouse stock with 8 pair-matings per generation and minimal inbreeding. The plan, however, cannot be strictly adhered to because some pairs fail to provide the two offspring required. In one particular generation the 8 matings provided the following numbers of offspring that were used as parents: 0, 1, 1, 2, 2, 3, 3, 4. What was the effective population size in this generation?

[Solution 123]

9

4.6   The breeding plan for each of the lines of the mouse stock described in Problem 3.6 was to mate 8 pairs and to use 2 offspring from each pair as parents of the next generation. If this plan had been strictly adhered to, what would have been the effective population size of the lines? What was actually the effective population size indicated by the data in Problem 3.6?

[Solution 133]

5 SMALL POPULATIONS:
III. Pedigreed populations and close inbreeding

Mi

5.1 What are the inbreeding coefficients in the offspring of marriages between the following relatives? (1) single first cousins, (2) double first cousins, (3) uncle–niece.

[Solution 4]

Ma

5.2 What is the coancestry of the children of a pair of identical twins married to unrelated individuals?

[Solution 14]

Mc

5.3 The following is a human pedigree of the absence of the corpus callosum. In generation I, individuals 1 and 4 are full sibs and so are 2 and 3. In generation IV, X represents a family of eight with two affected individuals. Calculate the inbreeding coefficient of this family and that of its parent, III 2.

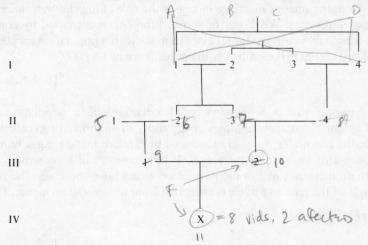

Data from Shapira, Y. & Cohen, T. (1973) *J. Med. Genet.*, **10**, 266–9.

[Solution 24]

5.4 If a predominantly self-fertilizing plant regularly cross-pollinates with a frequency of 1 per cent, what will be the frequency of heterozygotes at a 2-allele locus with gene frequencies of 0.2 and 0.8, assuming no selection?

[Solution 34]

5.5 Suppose that a population of a predominantly self-fertilizing plant is polymorphic for two alleles, *a* and *b*, and the frequencies of the three genotypes are

aa	ab	bb
0.54	0.12	0.34

What frequency of cross-pollination does this indicate, assuming there is no selection?

[Solution 44]

5.6 What would be the inbreeding coefficient after one generation of double first-cousin mating followed by three generations of full-sib mating?

[Solution 54]

5.7 Two highly inbred lines of a plant are crossed to produce an F_1 generation. The F_1 individuals are selfed to produce an F_2. Individuals of the F_2 are then backcrossed to the F_1 and to one of the inbred lines. What are the inbreeding coefficients of the progeny of these two backcrosses?

[Solution 64]

5.8 Consanguineous marriage increases the risk of the children suffering from recessive diseases. Work out how much the risk is increased by cousin marriage (single first cousins) for (1) cystic fibrosis with a population incidence of 1/2,500 and (2) phenylketonurea with an incidence of 1/11,000.

[Solution 74]

5.9 Suppose that a proportion, *y*, of individuals in a population are produced by consanguineous matings giving them all an inbreeding coefficient of *F*, while the remainder, $1-y$, are produced by random mating, e.g. a human population with some cousin marriages. If homozygotes of a recessive gene occur with an incidence of *I* in the population as a whole, show that the gene frequency, *q*, of the recessive allele is estimated from the overall incidence, *I*, by

$$(1-yF)q^2 + yFq = I$$

[Solution 84]

6 CONTINUOUS VARIATION

6.1 The figures tabulated are the number of leaves per plant in 25 F_1 and 25 F_2 plants from a cross of two cultivated varieties of tobacco, which had mean leaf numbers of 15.0 and 17.9 respectively. Tabulate (and plot if desired) the frequency distributions of the F_1 and F_2 generations. From each distribution calculate the mean, the variance, and the standard error of the mean. What is the main difference between the two distributions?

F_1					F_2				
18	15	16	18	15	16	20	19	17	14
16	14	16	18	17	16	14	14	15	17
16	13	16	14	16	20	13	12	15	16
15	16	15	15	16	21	18	15	14	18
15	16	16	15	16	14	17	13	15	13

Data from Johnson J. (1919) *Genetics*, **4**, 307–40.

[Solution 5]

6.2 The table gives the weights (g) at 60 days of age of 50 male mice, bred from 12 pairs of parents, in one generation of a strain that had been bred selectively for small size. Tabulate (and plot if desired) the frequency distribution and calculate the mean and variance. What is peculiar about the distribution?

12.8	15.7	13.7	5.7	6.1	13.2	12.5	7.0	6.6	14.8
12.8	14.1	14.0	17.8	14.7	11.8	13.5	14.1	16.2	6.6
5.7	11.7	13.4	6.6	6.8	15.6	13.0	11.5	12.1	15.4
11.8	11.4	10.7	15.6	14.9	4.7	13.1	13.4	14.5	13.4
11.8	17.2	15.0	15.1	14.6	14.8	15.1	14.9	18.4	16.5

Data kindly supplied by Dr J. W. B. King.

[Solution 15]

6.3 Work out the frequency distribution of the genotypic classes, from which to construct a histogram (like Fig. 6.1 in the *Introduction to Quantitative Genetics*), when a metric character is affected by 4 independently segregating loci, each with 2 alleles and complete dominance. The recessive alleles when homozygous each reduce the measurement by 1 unit. All recessive alleles have a gene frequency of 0.3.

[Solution 25]

6.4 Work out the frequency distribution with everything the same as in Problem 6.3 except that the frequencies of the recessive alleles are 0.3 at two of the loci and 0.7 at the other two.

[Solution 35]

6.5 Work out the frequency distribution when there are three loci, each with 2 alleles and with no dominance. At all loci, homozygotes differ by 2 units of measurement and heterozygotes differ by 1 unit from both homozygotes. At all loci the gene frequency of the allele that decreases the measurement is 0.4.

[Solution 45]

6.6 What gene frequency would produce a perfectly symmetrical distribution of measurement classes under the conditions of (1) Problem 6.3 and (2) Problem 6.5?

[Solution 55]

3,69

7 VALUES AND MEANS

M

7.1 Three allelic variants of the red cell acid phosphatase enzyme were present in a sample from the population in England. The table below gives the genotypes with their frequencies in the sample and the mean enzyme activity of each genotype. (CC individuals were not found.) What is the mean enzyme activity in this population?

Genotype	Frequency (%)	Enzyme activity
AA	9.6	122
AB	48.3	154
BB	34.3	188
AC	2.8	184
BC	5.0	212

Data from Spencer, N., *et al.* (1964) *Nature*, **201**, 299–300.

[Solution 6]

Mb

7.2 With the enzyme activities of the red cell acid phosphatase genotypes given in Problem 7.1 calculate the mean enzyme activities in populations with the C allele absent and the following gene frequencies of A : (1) 0.2, (2) 0.5, (3) 0.8.

[Solution 16]

ne

7.3 If there were a locus, overdominant with respect to a metric character, with the genotypic values given below, what gene frequency would give a random-mating population its maximum mean value, and what would the mean be?

A_1A_1	A_1A_2	A_2A_2
110	150	90

[Solution 26]

M

7.4 Example 7.3 describes the effects of two colour genes on the number of pigment granules in the hairs of mice. The brown gene, b, when homozygous, reduced the number of granules from 95 to 90, and the extreme dilute gene, c^e, reduced the number from 95 to 38. The genes' effects in combination were additive. Assuming both genes to be completely recessive, find what would be the mean granule number in a population with the b gene at a frequency of 0.5 and the c^e gene at a frequency of 0.2.

[Solution 36]

7.5 What are the average effects of the two alleles, and the average effect of the gene substitution, in the populations specified in Problem 7.2?

[Solution 46]

7.6 What are the breeding values of the three genotypes in the three populations specified in Problem 7.2?

[Solution 56]

7.7 Find the breeding values and dominance deviations of the three genotypes in the population specified in Problem 7.3, when the mean is at its maximal value.

[Solution 66]

7.8 Calculate the breeding value and the dominance deviation of the genotype bb $c^e c^e$ in the population specified in Problem 7.4. Give the breeding value both as a deviation from the population mean and in absolute units of granule number.

[Solution 76]

7.9 Problem 7.4 dealt with the effects of two colour genes on the number of pigment granules in mouse hairs. Example 7.7 describes the effects of the same two genes on the size of the pigment granules, and in this case the effects are not additive. Work out the interaction deviations of the genotypes in a population in which the bb homozygote has a frequency of 0.4 and the $c^e c^e$ homozygote a frequency of 0.2. Since both genes are assumed to be completely recessive the dominant homozygote and the heterozygote in each case have the same value and can be treated as one genotype, so that there are four genotypes whose interaction deviations are to be found. It will be useful for a later Problem if the values of the four genotypes given in Example 7.7 are first converted to deviations from the population mean; this may also make the logic clearer.

[Solution 86]

8 VARIANCE

8.1 The variance of leaf number in the F_1 and F_2 generations of a cross of tobacco varieties were calculated in problem 6.1. The variances were 1.46 in the F_1 and 5.97 in the F_2. Estimate the degree of genetic determination in the F_2 generation. What assumptions have to be made to do this?

[Solution 7]

8.2 Calculate the amounts of additive genetic and dominance variance arising from the genes referred to in the populations specified in (1) Problems 7.2 and 7.5 (all three populations), (2) Problems 7.3 and 7.7, (3) Problems 7.4 and 7.8.

[Solution 17]

8.3 Work out the proportion of the total genetic variance that is due to dominance, i.e. V_D/V_G, when the variance is caused by a single locus with the following degrees of dominance. (1) $d = \frac{1}{2}a$, i.e. incomplete dominance, (2) $d = a$, i.e. complete dominance, and (3) $d = 2a$, i.e. overdominance. The ratio V_D/V_G depends on the gene frequency. Plot graphs to show this relationship in each case and find from the graphs the approximate maximum value of the ratio and the gene frequency at which this occurs.

[Solution 27]

8.4 Refer to Problem 7.9 and its solution. Work out the three components of genetic variance, i.e. V_A, V_D, and V_I, attributable to the two genes in the population specified. Express each component as a percentage of the total genetic variance, V_G.

[Solution 37]

8.5 A sample of ten female mice from a random bred strain had the following numbers of live young born in their first and second litters.

Mouse	1	2	3	4	5	6	7	8	9	10
1st litter	11	9	13	10	9	8	10	11	10	13
2nd litter	10	12	12	10	8	6	12	9	12	12

(1) From this sample calculate the repeatability of litter size.
(2) What would you predict as being the expected size of the second litters of other mice from the same strain which had first litters of (a) 14 and (b) 5?

[Solution 47]

8.6 In a study of the fertility of pigs the litter sizes of 156 sows each of which had 10 litters were subjected to an analysis of variance with the following result. (The item 'Litter order' refers to differences between means of litters of the same order, first, second, third, etc.)

Source	d.f.	Mean square
Between sows	155	25.56
Litter order	9	93.95
Within sows	1395	3.23

(1) Calculate the repeatability of litter size.
(2) Suppose that you are planning a breeding programme for which a high heritability (V_A/V_P) is desirable. The fertility of individual sows can be measured by one litter, or with greater precision by the mean of several litters. By how much would the heritability be increased if fertility were measured as the mean of the first 2 litters, the first 3, and the first 4 litters? Assume that the repeatability is the same as that estimated from 10 litters.

Data from Olbrycht, T. M. (1943) *J. Agric. Sci.*, **33**, 28–84.

[Solution 57]

9 RESEMBLANCE BETWEEN RELATIVES

M¹

9.1 What is the coefficient of relationship, r, between the children of a pair of MZ twins married to unrelated spouses?

[Solution 8]

Ma

9.2 Problems 7.4, 7.8 and 8.2 (3) dealt with the effects of two genes on the pigmentation of mouse hairs in a specified population. Suppose that the measurements of individuals were subject to environmental variance amounting to one third of the total genetic variance, but that there were no environmental differences between family means. What would then be the phenotypic resemblance between the following relatives in this population: (1) Offspring and mid-parent, (2) Offspring and one parent, (3) full sibs, (4) half sibs, (5) double first cousins?

[Solution 18]

9.3 The following correlations of total finger-ridge counts have been reported. Are they consistent with each other? What assumptions have to be made in comparing the correlations?

Midparent–child: $r = 0.69 \pm 0.03$
Father–child: $r = 0.50 \pm 0.04$
Mother–child: $r = 0.49 \pm 0.04$ — no maternal effects

Data from Holt, S. B. (1956/57) *Acta genet.*, **6**, 473–6.

[Solution 28]

relationship r b_op and ¹⁹ r_op ?

M\ **9.4**   The estimates below refer to the litter size of mice under different experimental procedures. In one case all litters were standardized at birth to 8 young by removing young in excess of 8 or fostering young from other litters to make up to 8. In the other case the litters were not manipulated and most of the young born were reared to weaning. Suggest reasons, other than sampling error and strain differences, that might account for the differences between the estimates. In both cases the full sibs were litter mates.

	Litters standardized	Litters not standardized
Full-sib correlation	0.055	0.107
Daughter–dam regression	0.045	−0.028

Data from Eisen, E. J. (1978) *Genetics*, **88**, 781–811; Falconer, D. S. (1965) pp. 763–74 in Geerts, S. J. (ed.), *Genetics Today*. Proc. XI Internat. Congr. Genetics, Vol. **3**. Pergamon, Oxford.

[Solution 38]

10 HERITABILITY

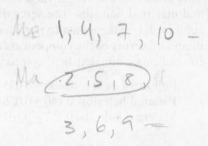

10.1 What would be the heritability estimated from each of the following correlations or regressions, assuming that resemblance due to environment or dominance was negligible? *Table 10.2*

(1) Regression of offspring on father	$= 0.21$
(2) Regression of offspring on mother	$= 0.27$
(3) Correlation of full sibs	$= 0.34$
(4) Regression of offspring on mean of parents	$= 0.32$
(5) Correlation of half sibs	$= 0.02$
(6) Regression of female offspring on mother's sister	$= 0.03$
(7) Regression of daughters on dams, within sires	$= 0.09$

[Solution 48]

10.2 The following data were obtained in a study of the adult height of people in two West African villages. Female heights were adjusted to male equivalents so that the means were the same in males and females. Derive what you regard as the most reliable estimate of the heritability, and its standard error. What other component of covariance, in addition to V_A, can be derived from the data?

	Offspring–parent regressions ±standard errors		
	Father	Mother	Mid-parent
Sons	0.323 ± 0.058	0.454 ± 0.057	0.705 ± 0.085
Daughters	0.291 ± 0.044	0.420 ± 0.048	0.638 ± 0.063
Both	0.303 ± 0.036	0.424 ± 0.038	0.654 ± 0.052

Standard deviations (inches): Males 2.5; Females 2.3

Data from Roberts, D. F. *et al.* (1978) *Ann. Hum. Genet.*, **42**, 15–24.

[Solution 58]

10.3 In the study used for Problem 10.2 the sib correlations given below were also obtained, the marriage customs of the people providing both paternal and maternal half sibs. The sexes did not differ in their correlations and are combined. Use these data to partition the variance of height in this population. (Standard errors of the components are not given in the solution.) How do the components estimated here compare with those estimated in Problem 10.2?

Full sibs   0.406 ± 0.035
Paternal half sibs   0.140 ± 0.056
Maternal half sibs   0.257 ± 0.101

[Solution 68]

10.4   Show that the intraclass correlation of twins can be estimated from an analysis of variance by $t = (B - W)/(B + W)$, where B and W are the mean squares between pairs and within pairs respectively.

[Solution 78]

10.5   Skin-fold thickness provides a useful measure of (human) fatness. The table gives the correlation of skin-fold thickness in twins aged under 10 and between 10 and 15. Estimate the heritabilities in the two groups. What can be deduced about resemblance due to common environment?

	Under 10	10–15
MZ	0.64	0.91
DZ	0.38	0.42

Data from Brook, C. G. C. *et al.* (1975) *Brit. Med. J.*, **1975**, **2**, 719–21.

[Solution 88]

10.6   The table gives the mean squares from an analysis of variance of a random-breeding population of *Drosophila melanogaster*. The character was the number of sternopleural bristles. These are bristles on the sides of the thorax, the numbers on one side being counted. There were 62 males (sires) each mated to 3 females (dams). Each female laid eggs in one vial. The bristles of 10 male and 10 female offspring of each dam were counted. Calculate the correlation of half sibs and of full sibs, and estimate the components of variance that can be separated by these data.

	Males	Females
Between sires	3.894	4.461
Between dams within sires	2.198	2.061
Within dams	1.125	0.893

Data from Sheridan, A. K. *et al.* (1968) *Theor. Appl. Genet.*, **38**, 179–87.

[Solution 98]

10.7 Show that if the correlation of full sibs is 0.75, the heritability of the character cannot be greater than 0.5. The full-sib correlation of weaning weight in mice is 0.8; what is the maximum heritability compatible with this?

[Solution 108]

10.8 A study of morphological variation in a population of *Geospiza fortis*, one of Darwin's Finches in the Galapagos, provides the following data on the depth of the bill. How would you interpret these data?

Regressions, ±s.e.
    Offspring–midparent   0.82±0.15
    Offspring–father   0.47±0.17
    Offspring–mother   0.48±0.13
Correlations, ±s.e.
    Full sibs   0.71±0.12
    Father–mother   0.33

Data from Boag, P. T. & Grant, P. R. (1978) *Nature*, **274**, 793–4.

[Solution 118]

10.9 Suppose that a population has bred with assortative mating for long enough to reach equilibrium. There is a correlation of $r=0.4$ between mates, the choice of mates being based purely on phenotypic values of a particular character. The correlation of full sibs with respect to this character is $t=0.3$. The character is known to have negligible dominance variance and to be negligibly affected by environment common to sibs. What is the estimate of the heritability in the population, and what would the heritability be if there were no assortative mating?

[Solution 128]

10.10 If the heritabilities given below were estimated by the methods indicated, and in every case the total number of individuals measured was 400, what would be approximately the standard errors of the estimates, assuming that there was no environmental resemblance between sibs, and that the data came from unselected individuals of a random breeding population?

(1) $h^2=0.5$, from regression of sons on fathers; 200 fathers.
(2) $h^2=0.6$, from regression of the mean of 3 offspring (full sibs) on the mean of their parents.
(3) $h^2=0.4$, from correlation of full sibs in families of 5.
(4) $h^2=0.2$, from correlation of half sibs in 20 families of half sibs with no full sibs among them.

[Solution 138]

11 SELECTION:
I. The response and its prediction

11.1 What would be the expected rate of progress per generation if selection were applied to the characters in the table, individuals being selected on the basis of their own phenotypic merit?

		Heritability	Phenotypic variance	Proportion selected (%)
(1)	Body weight of mice (g)	0.37	10.7	(a) 25
				(b) 50
				(c) 75
(2)	Development time in *Tribolium* (days)	0.18	1.7	10
(3)	Female fertility of mice (litter size)	0.22	4.3	30

[Solution 9]

11.2 The species of Darwin's Finch in Problem 10.8 suffered severe mortality as a result of a drought in 1977. This species eats seeds, and the seeds available during the drought were mainly large and hard ones. The surviving birds, in comparison with the population before the drought, were larger in several dimensions, particularly of the bill. The mean depth of the bill in 642 birds before the drought was 9.42 mm and in 85 birds after the drought was 9.96 mm. What change in bill depth would you predict from this selective survival and the data in Problem 10.8?

Data from Boag, P. T. & Grant, P. R. (1981) *Science*, **214**, 82–4.

[Solution 19]

11.3 Suppose that selection for weight gain from 5 to 9 weeks in a flock of broiler chickens is planned. From the following data predict the mean weight gain after five generations of selection. In each generation 4 males and 8 females will be selected, each out of 60 birds measured. Base population: mean = 738 g, standard deviation 111 g, heritability (from sib analysis) = 0.81.

Data based on Pym, R. A. E. & Nichols, P. J. (1979) *Brit.Poult. Sci.*, **20**, 73–86.

[Solution 29]

11.4   The data in the table refer to selection for increased and for decreased plasma cholesterol levels in mice. Calculate the realized heritability from the two lines separately and from the divergence. M = generation mean, P = mean of selected individuals to be used as parents of the next generation. The units are log (mg/100 ml). The sexes are averaged.

	High		Low	
Generation	M	P	M	P
0	2.16	2.32	2.16	2.02
1	2.26	2.34	2.06	2.00
2	2.26	2.37	2.03	1.97
3	2.33	2.41	2.02	1.96
4	2.45	2.47	2.05	2.01
5	2.44	—	2.01	—

Data from Weibust, R. S. (1973) *Genetics*, **73**, 303–12.

[Solution 39]

11.5   The table gives the data on the selection of mice for small body size in the last generation of the experiment shown in Fig. 11.5. Calculate the un-weighted and the weighted selection differentials. Treat female and male parents separately and then combine them. What conclusion can be drawn about natural selection? ⌐ acct how many prog leaves

Mating number	Weights (g) of parents		Number of offspring measured
	Female	Male	
1	7.6	12.4	1
2	12.4	14.5	9
3	13.5	11.6	0
4	13.7	11.6	15
5	13.2	14.3	5
6	17.2	17.1	14
7	10.7	13.8	10
8	12.9	11.6	9
9	14.2	10.1	0
10	10.5	13.1	6

Mean of population from which parents were selected:
Females, 13.14;   Males, 14.80

[Solution 49]

11.6   Suppose that you are selecting sheep for growth rate in an experiment with the following procedure. Equal numbers of males and females are selected and mated in single pairs, the numbers selected being large. Both sexes breed first when they are 2 years old, and subsequently produce lambs once each year. The average number of lambs reared to maturity is 1.2 per ewe per breeding season. Equal numbers are selected each year. For how many years should you keep the parents before replacing them by selected offspring in order to maximize the rate of progress per year? What proportion of lambs will then be selected in each year?

[Solution 59]

11.7   The breeding scheme for sheep in Problem 11.6 is not a practically realistic one. To be more realistic, assume that instead of mating each male to only one female, males are mated each to 10 females. This affects the optimal procedure which is now to discard females when they are 4 years old, having had 3 breeding seasons, and to discard males when they are 3 years old, having had 2 breeding seasons. How much better would this be than the optimal procedure with single-pair matings? Why is the optimal age for discarding both sexes lower than in Problem 11.6?

[Solution 111]

11.8   If sows are to be selected for litter size, selection can be based on the size of their first litter or on the mean size of two or more litters. Increasing the number of litters has the advantages of increasing the intensity of selection and of increasing the heritability, but it has the disadvantage of increasing the generation length. What is the optimum number of litters for maximizing the expected response per year? Take the repeatability of litter size to be 0.409 from Problem 8.6. Assume that (i) sows have their first litters when they are 1 year old and subsequently have litters at 6-month intervals, (ii) the average number of individuals reared per litter is 8, (iii) the number selected is the number required to replace the parents. For simplicity, assume further that (iv) the number selected is large and (v) generations are non-overlapping, the offspring of selected individuals all having their first litters when the youngest is 1 year old.

[Solution 121]

11.9   Suppose that one of the genes affecting sternopleural bristle score in *Drosophila* is additive, that the two homozygotes differ by 0.3 bristles, and that the increasing allele is at a frequency of 0.4. What will be the frequency of this allele after the 10 per cent highest-scoring flies have been selected in two successive generations in a population with a phenotypic standard deviation of 2.0 bristles?

[Solution 131]

12 SELECTION: II. The results of experiments

murk

12.1 Calculate the quantities listed in Table 12.2 from the results of the following experiment. (The last two quantities will have to be based on a guess.) Mice were selected for increased 3–6 week weight gain over 43 generations. There was no selection for decreased gain but there was an unselected control. The response was linear over the first 19 generations and reached a limit at about generation 34. The data needed are in the table, males and females being averaged. The figures in parentheses are the generations to which the data refer.

Realized heritability (1–19)	0.20
Phenotypic standard deviation (1–19)	2.10 g
Mean selection differential per generation (1–19)	2.25 g
Mean of selected line (34–43)	23.55 g
Mean of control line (34–43)	11.90 g
Effective population size	33

Data from Barria, N. & Bradford, G. E. (1981) *J. Anim. Sci.*, **52**, 729–38.

[Solution 67]

I3 SELECTION:
III. Information from relatives

12.1

13.1 Calculate the heritability of family means, h_f^2, and of within-family deviations, h_w^2, for characters with the following parameters. Calculate also the expected responses to family selection and to within-family selection, relative in each case to the response to individual selection, i.e. R_f/R and R_w/R, assuming equal intensities of selection.

	Individual heritability	Type of family	Sib correlation	Family size
(1)	0.1	Half sibs	0.025	10
(2)	0.1	Half sibs	0.025	20
(3)	0.1	Full sibs	0.5	4
(4)	0.2	Full sibs	0.8	4
(5)	0.2	Full sibs	0.8	8

[Solution 77]

13.2 Daily weight gain in British Large White pigs has a half-sib correlation of 0.10 and a full-sib correlation of 0.36. Compare the expected rates of progress, relative to that of individual selection, when selection is based on

(1) The mean of 5 half sibs, all from different dams, the selected individual being one of the five.
(2) The mean of 5 full sibs, which include the selected individual.
(3) The mean of 5 full sibs, which exclude the selected individual.
(4) The individual's deviation from the mean of its 5 full sibs, which include itself.

Data from Smith, C. *et al.* (1962) *Anim. Prod.*, **4**, 128–43.

[Solution 87]

13.3 What would be the appropriate index for selecting pigs for daily weight gain on the basis of the individual's gain and the family mean of 5 full sibs, the individual being included in the family mean? Take the full-sib correla-

28

tion to be 0.36 as in Problem 13.2.

[Solution 97]

13.4 If the figures below were the daily weight gains of four individual pigs from different full-sib families, what would be their order of merit according to the index worked out in Problem 13.3 with any necessary modification for the numbers of sibs?

Pig	Weight gain		Number in family
	Individual	Family mean	
A	1.6	1.3	5
B	1.5	1.6	5
C	1.5	1.6	8
D	1.3	1.7	8

Population mean = 1.5

[Solution 107]

13.5 If selection for daily weight gain in pigs were applied by the index calculated in Problem 13.3, how would the expected response compare with the response expected from individual selection?

[Solution 117]

13.6 Construct an index for selecting bulls for milk yield on the basis of the yields of the mother and 10 paternal half sisters. Assume that the half sisters all have different mothers which are not related to the bull's mother. Assume also that there is no environmental correlation between half sibs. Take the heritability of milk yield to be 0.35 (Table 10.1), though this is higher than most estimates.

[Solution 127]

13.7 Predict the rate of improvement of milk yield per generation if 1 in 20 bulls were selected by the index of Problem 13.6, and 1 in 2 cows were selected on their own yield. Take the phenotypic standard deviation of milk yield to be 696 kg (Example 8.7), and assume that the selection is made from a large number measured.

[Solution 137]

14

INBREEDING AND CROSSBREEDING:
I. Changes of mean value

Mike

14.1 Suppose that a random-bred population of maize had a mean yield of 140 g per plant, and that four loci with known effects on yield were segregating. What would be the inbreeding depression caused by these loci after one generation of self-pollination, if the gene effects were as given below? The gene effects in each case are the differences in yield (g per plant) between the genotype listed and the 'AA' homozygote; the gene frequency is that of the 'a' allele.

Locus	Difference from AA		q_a
	Aa	aa	
(1)	− 10	− 20	0.5
(2)	+ 5	− 30	0.5
(3)	− 20	− 30	0.2
(4)	0	− 60	0.1

[Solution 69]

Mark

14.2 If inbreeding with selection in the maize population specified in Problem 14.1 succeeded in fixing the more favourable allele at each of the four loci, by how much would the yield be increased?

[Solution 79]

14.3 From the data on mouse litter size in Example 14.2 calculate how much inbreeding depression of litter size results from inbreeding in the mother and how much from inbreeding in the litter. Assume that both are linear with respect to F, and that the maternal and litter effects combine additively. What would be the predicted litter size if mice could be inbred to $F = 100$ per cent without any selection operating?

[Solution 89]

Mike

14.4 Use the results of Problem 14.3 to predict the total inbreeding depression of litter size when the inbreeding coefficient of the mothers is 0.56

and that of the litters is 0.64. These were the inbreeding coefficients in the last generation of the experiment depicted in Fig. 14.2 (a). This was a different experiment from that of Example 14.2 used in Problem 14.3. How well do the two experiments agree?

mark

[Solution 99]

14.5   A control line of mice was kept for 30 generations and its litter size showed no evidence of inbreeding depression in spite of its effective population size being not greater than 40. One possible reason for the absence of inbreeding depression is that there may have been some inadvertent selection for litter size. The mating system was intended to be minimal inbreeding, one young female being taken at random from each family. In theory no selection was possible, but minimal inbreeding cannot be applied strictly in practice because some families contain no surviving female. Replacements have then to be taken from other families, and some selection can be caused by these replacements. How much selection would have been needed to counteract inbreeding depression at the rate expected from the solution of Problem 14.3? The selection resulting from replacements would have been individual selection, and the realized heritability appropriate to individual selection was estimated in the same strain to be 0.22.

Data from Falconer, D. S. (1960) *J. Cell. Comp. Physiol.*, **56** (*Suppl.* 1), 153–67.

MC

[Solution 109]

14.6   Crosses were made between varieties of cultivated tomatoes, which are normally self-fertilizing. The mean weights (kg) of fruit produced per plant in a three-week period by the parental varieties and the F_1 in two crosses were as follows.

Cross	P_1	P_2	F_1
(1)	1.44	1.36	1.41 $\simeq \bar{x}$ of $P_1 + P_2$
(2)	1.28	0.88	1.42 $> \bar{x}$

What would be the predicted yields of the F_2 generations, and of the F_3 generations produced by selfing the F_2?

Data from Williams, W. (1960) *Genetics*, **45**, 1457–65.

Mike

[Solution 119]

14.7   In Problem 6.1 the mean leaf numbers in the F_1 and F_2 generations of a cross of two varieties of tobacco were calculated. The mean of the F_1 was 15.72 ± 0.24 and the mean of the F_2 was 15.84 ± 0.49. Without knowing the leaf numbers in the parental varieties, what can you conclude about the heterosis shown by the F_1?

[Solution 129]

15 INBREEDING AND CROSSBREEDING: II. Changes of variance

15.1 The genetic variance of abdominal bristle number in *Drosophila* is predominantly additive (Table 8.2). If a random-breeding population, in which the phenotypic variance was 4.0 and the heritability 52 per cent, were inbred by full-sib mating in a large number of lines without selection, what would be the components of variance between lines and within lines: (1) after 1 generation, (2) after 3 generations, and (3) when the inbreeding coefficient was 95 per cent? If mass selection were applied for one generation when the inbreeding coefficient was 95 per cent, what would be the realized heritability of the response? (Mass selection means selecting individuals without regard to their line.)

[Solution 75]

15.2 Consider again the inbred *Drosophila* population of Problem 15.1. What would be the expected response to one generation of selection carried out in the following manner after three generations of inbreeding, when $F = 0.5$? There are many lines, each consisting of a single full-sib family. Four flies, two of each sex, are taken at random from each line; the best 5 per cent of the lines are selected on the basis of the mean of the 4 flies sampled from them; the 4 flies from each of the selected lines are then mated with their sibs and the progeny are measured.

[Solution 85]

15.3 The body size of *Drosophila*, measured as thorax length, has little non-additive genetic variance (Table 8.2). Suppose that the heritability of thorax length was found to be 0.34 in a stock that was maintained by random mating among large numbers but had recently been started from a single pair of flies. What would be the estimate of the heritability in the population from which the original pair was taken?

[Solution 95]

15.4 Minor differences in the skeleton are common in mice. Twenty-seven characters of which variants occur were studied in sublines of the C57BL inbred strain. Two particular sublines were found to differ in respect of 5 of the

27 characters, and each difference was attributed to one mutational step. The strain had been inbred by full-sib mating for 40 or more generations before separation of the sublines. After separation, one of the sublines had a further 21 generations, and the other had 29 generations, of full-sib mating at the time of the study. If the differences did arise from mutation, how would these results be interpreted in terms of the number of loci at which mutations can affect the characters and their mutation rates?

Data from Deol, M. S. *et al.* (1975) *J. Morph.*, **100**, 345–76.

[Solution 105]

15.5   The following estimates of the parameters of individual plant yield were made in an open-pollinated variety of maize.

Mean $= 308$ g; $V_P = 5798$; $V_A = 864$; $V_D = 188$

If this population were inbred without any selection and the lines were crossed (1) when the inbreeding coefficient was 50 per cent, and (2) when the inbreeding coefficient was virtually 100 per cent, what would be the phenotypic components of variance between crosses and within crosses? Assume that $V_I = 0$, and that environmental differences between crosses were eliminated by the experimental design.

If each cross mean were estimated from measurements of 20 individual plants, what would be the variance of the observed means of crosses?

Data from Gardner, C. O. (1977) pp. 475–89 in Pollak, E. *et al.* (eds), *Proc. Int. Conf. Quantitative Genetics.* Iowa State Univ., Ames, Iowa, USA.

[Solution 115]

15.6   Consider again the crosses in Problem 15.5. If 50 crosses were made at each stage, what would you predict the highest observed mean yield among the 50 crosses to be? If this best cross were then repeated, and a new set of plants from it were grown and measured, what would you predict the mean yield to be, assuming that there was no environmental difference between the first and second determinations of its yield?

[Solution 125]

15.7 A diallel cross, without reciprocals, was made between five varieties of the bean *Phaseolus aureus*, which is normally self-pollinating. The mean yields in grams per plant of the crosses are given below. The varieties are designated A to E and their yields are also given (on the diagonal), although these are not needed for this Problem. Calculate (1) the general combining ability of each variety, and (2) the deviation from expectation of each cross, i.e. the specific combining ability + error. Plot a scatter diagram like Fig. 15.4.

	A	B	C	D	E
A	9.7	14.1	22.8	16.9	31.8
B	—	3.3	16.5	6.2	12.4
C	—	—	9.0	8.3	9.2
D	—	—	—	6.8	13.1
E	—	—	—	—	12.5

Data from Singh, K. B. & Jain, R. P. (1971) *Theor. Appl. Genet.*, **41**, 279–81.

[Solution 135]

16 INBREEDING AND CROSSBREEDING: III. Applications

16.1 If you were to make a three-way cross and a four-way cross of the varieties in Problem 15.7, which varieties would you choose, and how would you make the crosses, in order to get the highest predicted yields? What would the predicted yields be?

[Solution 96]

16.2 A 'rotational cross' with two breeds or lines, A and B, is made as follows, where X always refers to the crossbred generation.

(1) $A \times B$
(2) $X_1 \times A$
(3) $X_2 \times B$
(4) $X_3 \times A$

Calculate the expected performance of the crossbred progeny in each generation up to (4), in terms of the purebred and single-cross performances, assuming no epistatic interaction and no maternal effects.

[Solution 106]

16.3 A rotational cross with 3 breeds, A, B, C, is made as follows, where X again represents the crossbred progeny.

(1) $A \times B$
(2) $X_1 \times C$
(3) $X_2 \times A$
(4) $X_3 \times B$
(5) $X_4 \times C$

Calculate the expected performance of each generation in terms of the purebred and single-cross performances, assuming the absence of epistasis and maternal effects.

[Solution 116]

16.4 Suppose that all the single crosses of the lines used in rotational

35

crossing show the same amount of heterosis. What proportion of this single-cross heterosis will be attained in successive generations of the rotational cross? Work this out for the four generations of the two-line rotational cross in Problem 16.2 and for the five generations of the three-line rotational cross in Problem 16.3.

[Solution 126]

16.5   When rotational crossbreeding is applied to animals the females used for crossing are always crossbred and the males always purebred. The system then has the useful feature that the pure breeds themselves need produce no more females than are required for replacements. The data below are the mean weights of individual pigs at 154 days (W) and the mean number of pigs per litter at 154 days (N), in three breeds, Chester White (C), Duroc (D) and Yorkshire (Y), and their single crosses. From the solution of Problem 16.3 calculate the expected mean total weight per litter in each of the 5 generations of rotational crossing, starting with (Y$\female$ × C$\male$)$\female$× D$\male$. Make the simplifying assumptions that the number in the litter depends only on the mother's genotype and the weight depends only on the individual's genotype, and that epistasis is negligible.

	C	D	Y	CD	CY	DY
W (kg)	78	88	84	92	90	96
N	6.6	6.3	7.9	7.4	8.2	7.3

Data from Schneider, J. F. (1978) *Ph.D. Thesis*, Iowa State Univ., Ames, Iowa, USA.

[Solution 136]

17 SCALE

Mi

17.1   Figure 17.2 (*Introduction to Quantitative Genetics*) shows data where a transformation to logarithms is indicated if equality of the variances of the three lines is desired. What would be the standard deviations of log-weights? The data show a large amount of asymmetry in the responses to selection. Would this asymmetry be removed by transformation to logs?

[Solution 10]

Mc

17.2   The data below are the 6-week weights (g) of mice from selected strains of different body weights and crosses of these strains. There were three 'size groups', large, control and small. In each size group there were six replicate lines. (Figure 12.1 refers to these lines.) Crosses were made between lines of the same size group and between lines of different size groups. The object was to find out if the heterosis would be greater in crosses between lines of different size than in crosses within size groups. The first row of the table gives the mean weights of the replicates in each size group and the rest of the table gives the mean weights of the crosses, reciprocals averaged. How would the conclusions about the heterosis be altered by transformation of the means to logarithms?

	Large	Control	Small
Lines means	28.74	20.99	14.91
Large	30.68	26.00	21.85
Control	—	21.91	18.48
Small	—	—	14.84

handwritten annotations alongside table:
1.458   1.322   1.1735
1.4869   1.415   1.3395
          1.3406   1.2667
                    1.1714

Data from Kumar, C. K. B. (1980) *Ph.D. Thesis*, University of Edinburgh.

[Solution 20]

Mc

17.3   The table shows the mean number of sternopleural bristles in *Drosophila* males with different combinations of X chromosome and autosomes. There were two X chromosomes, one from a high bristle-number line and the other from a low bristle-number line. These two X chromosomes were put into the background of autosomes from lines at different levels of bristle number. There is a strong epistatic interaction between the X chromosomes and the autosomes. Can you find a scale transformation that will remove the interaction and make the X chromosome effect the same in all backgrounds? This is not straightforward. It is helpful to know that four of the bristles, two on each side, are larger than the others, different in structure, and never absent except when the mean is very low.

Autosomal background	Source of X chromosome		Difference H − L
	High	Low	
A	9.49	7.75	1.74
B	13.34	10.84	2.50
C	22.72	16.36	6.36
D	34.87	24.84	10.03
E	47.80	32.80	15.00

Data from McPhee, C. P. & Robertson, A. (1970) *Genet. Res.*, **16**, 1–16.

[Solution 30]

18 THRESHOLD CHARACTERS

Mi

18.1 A family study of congenital dislocation of the hip (human) gave the following results. There were altogether 397 'index patients' whose relatives were studied. The first-degree relatives were mostly parents and full sibs, the second-degree mostly grand-parents, uncles, aunts, nephews and nieces, and the third-degree were all first cousins. The numbers of relatives examined and the numbers affected with the malformation were as follows.

	Affected	Total
1st degree	35	1777
2nd degree	16	4746
3rd degree	8	4220

The incidence in the population as a whole was about 1 per 1000. From these data evaluate (approximately) the correlation of relatives of the three sorts with respect to liability, and estimate the heritability of liability. Which estimate of the heritability would you think likely to be the most reliable?

Data from Wynne-Davies (1970) pp. 316–38 in Emery, A. E. H. (ed.), *Modern Trends in Human Genetics* – **1**. Butterworths, London.

[Solution 94]

Mc

18.2 The data below come, somewhat simplified, from an analysis of twinning in Swedish Friesian cattle. Cows (or heifers) which had one twin birth were picked at random from the records. The proportions of their mothers and of their daughters that had twins in their fourth, fifth or sixth calvings were then found. These incidences and the incidence in the breed as a whole are given below. Of those cows which had twins at their first calving, the proportion that had twins in a later calving is given in the last line of the table. Calculate approximately the heritability and the repeatability of liability to produce twins.

Population	3.5%
Mothers	4.6%
Daughters	4.8%
Repeat calvings	10.0%

Data from Johansson, I. *et al.* (1974) *Hereditas*, **78**, 201–34.

[Solution 104]

18.3 An alternative way of analysing twinning is to treat it as 'litter size', individuals having a value 1 if they have single calves or 2 if they have twins. When analysed in this way the correlation of half sibs in the Swedish Friesians was found to be 0.0058. Is this consistent with the heritability of liability calculated in Problem 18.2?

[Solution 114]

18.4 Fleece-rot is a damaging condition in Australian Merino sheep, associated with wet weather. There is, however, genetic variation in susceptibility. The heritability of liability was estimated as 0.3 in a flock where the incidence was 23 per cent. Reducing the incidence is obviously desirable; increasing the incidence might be useful in an experimental flock. What would be the incidences after two generations of two-way selection, for reduced and for increased incidence, if 10 per cent of males and 50 per cent of females were selected on an individual basis?

Data kindly supplied by Kevin D. Atkins.

[Solution 124]

18.5 A form of polydactyly (extra fingers and toes) appeared in a strain of mice under selection for large size. At first it was at low frequency and only the hind feet were affected. Breeding from the affected individuals over a few generations increased the frequency and resulted in the appearance of individuals with hind and fore feet affected. There were thus three phenotypic classes: normal (*N*), hind feet only affected (*H*), and both hind and fore feet affected (*F*). The frequencies after 5 generations of selection were

N	H	F
20%	50%	30%

The progeny of different types of mating provided good evidence that *H* was intermediate in liability between *N* and *F*.

Calculate (1) the difference in liability between the two thresholds, in standard deviation units, (2) the mean of the population in threshold units, as a deviation from the threshold separating *N* from *H*, (3) the mean liability of each of the three phenotypes in threshold units as deviations from the population mean.

Data from Roberts, R. C. & Mendell, N. R. (1975) *Genet. Res.*, **191**, 427–44.

[Solution 134]

19 CORRELATED CHARACTERS

19.1 The data below are taken from a sib analysis in a flock of broiler chickens. They refer to the weight gain (G) from 5 to 9 weeks of individual males and the weight of food (F) consumed in the same period, both in units of grams. The figures given are the components of variance and of covariance between half-sib families, and the total phenotypic variances and covariance. From these data calculate the heritability of the two characters, and the phenotypic, genetic, and environmental correlations between them.

| | Variance | | Covariance |
	Weight-gain	Food consumption	G with F
Between sires	1602	6150	2229
Total	12321	61504	22848

Data based on Pym, R. A. E. & Nicholls, P. J. (1979) *Brit. Poult. Sci.*, **20**, 73–86.

[Solution 40]

19.2 The data refer to two characters of *Drosophila*: body size measured as thorax length, and fertility measured as the number of eggs laid in 4 days. The phenotypic variances and the covariance were measured in a genetically variable population and in a genetically uniform group consisting of F_1's of crosses between inbred lines. From these data, estimate the three correlations – phenotypic, genetic, and environmental – in the variable population. How does the meaning of the genetic correlation here differ from that of the genetic correlation in Problem 19.1?

| Population | Variances | | Covariance |
	Body size	Fertility	
Variable	0.366	43.4	0.87
Uniform	0.186	16.6	0.27

Data from Robertson, F. W. (1957) *J. Genet.*, **55**, 428–43.

[Solution 50]

19.3 Consider again the data on broiler chickens in Problem 19.1 Suppose that selection for increased weight gain is to be applied in one line and for increased food consumption in another line. The proportions selected in both lines are to be 10 per cent of males and 20 per cent of females. Calculate the predicted responses per generation of the two characters when directly selected and when responding as correlated characters.

[Solution 60]

19.4 Five generations of selection were applied to the broiler flock described in Problem 19.1. One line was selected for increased weight gain (G) and another was selected for increased food-consumption (F). The total selection differentials applied over the five generations and the total responses were as follows, the responses being deviations from a control line.

	Line selected for	
	G	F
Selection differential (g)	574	1312
Response of G (g)	186	120
Response of F (g)	412	525

Calculate the realized heritabilities of the two characters and the realized genetic correlation between them.

Data from Pym, R. A. E. & Nicholls, P. J. (1979) *Brit. Poult. Sci.*, **20**, 73–86.

[Solution 70]

19.5 The litter size of mice could be increased by selection of females for their litter size, or by selection of both sexes for body weight. Which would be the better of these two simple procedures, given the following parameters?

Heritability of litter size   = 0.22
Heritability of body weight = 0.35
Genetic correlation   = 0.43
Proportion selected: females = 25%
                            males = 10%

[Solution 80]

19.6 In addition to the two procedures for increasing litter size considered in Problem 19.5, a third procedure would be to select females for litter size and males for body weight. There are several ways in which this could be carried out. Assume the procedure to be as follows. Males are weighed at the appropriate age (e.g. six weeks) and 25 per cent are selected out of a large number. The selected males are each mated to a randomly chosen group of four young females whose litter sizes are not yet known. When the females have had their first litters the best one of the four mated to each male is selected. The litters of these selected males and females are reared as the next generation. How much better would this procedure be than selecting only on females for litter size? Take the heritabilities and genetic correlation to be as given in Problem 19.5.

[Solution 90]

19.7   The data refer to the broiler chickens described in Problem 19.1. Suppose that it is desired to improve 5–9 week growth (G), using the weight of food consumed (F) as an aid to the selection. Calculate the appropriate index for evaluating the parents to be selected. The estimates of the parameters needed are as follows. In order to have the decimal points conveniently placed for the calculations, the units of weight are changed here from grams to 100 g units.

	G	F
h^2	0.52	0.40
σ_P	1.11	2.48
r_A		0.71
r_P		0.83

[Solution 100]

19.8   If selection for growth were applied by the index calculated in Problem 19.7, what would be the predicted improvement per generation, assuming the intensity of selection was $i = 1.5775$ as in Problem 19.3? How much better would the index be for improving growth than selection for growth alone without the aid of a secondary character?

[Solution 110]

19.9   If selection for growth were applied by the index as in Problem 19.8, what would be the expected rate of change of the secondary character food consumption?

[Solution 120]

19.10   From the data and calculations in Problem 19.7 calculate an index for improving economic value, given that the value of growth is 8 cents per 100 g of weight gain, and that of food consumption is −2 cents per 100 g.

Data from Pym, R. A. E. & James, J. W. (1979) *Brit. Poult. Sci.*, **20**, 99–107.

[Solution 130]

19.11 Calculate the rate of improvement of economic value expected from selection by the index in Problem 19.10, when 10 per cent of males and 20 per cent of females are selected as in Problem 19.3. How much better would the index be for improving economic value than selection for growth alone?

[Solution 140]

20 METRIC CHARACTERS UNDER NATURAL SELECTION

20.1 Problem 11.2 was concerned with evolutionary change in a species of Darwin's Finch following selective survival with respect to bill depth. Prediction of the response to this natural selection was made from $R = h^2 S$ [11.2] on the assumption that 'the cause of the selective survival was the bill-depth itself and not some other character correlated with it'. Show that the prediction would be valid if

$$\frac{r_A}{r_P} = \frac{h_Y}{h_W}$$

where Y is bill depth and W is fitness, and the correlations are between bill depth and fitness.

[Solution 2]

20.2 A rough idea of the effect of natural selection on IQ score can be got from the following data on a sample of whites in Minnesota. The data refer to the IQ scores of individuals and the size of those individuals' completed families, i.e. the number of their children. It has to be assumed that family size is an adequate measure of fitness. The means, standard deviations, and heritabilities were

	Mean	s.d.	h^2
IQ score	103	15.4	0.6
Family size	3.4	2.3	0.1–0.2

The heritability of family size was not reliably estimated but was probably in the range indicated. The correlation between the two characters was $+0.11$. It has to be assumed that the genetic correlation was not different from the phenotypic correlation. On the basis of these data and assumptions, what is the predicted change of IQ score per generation? What would be the apparent, i.e. correlated, selection differential on IQ scores in this population?

Data from Waller, J. H. (1971) *Social Biol.*, **18**, 122–36.

[Solution 65]

45

20.3 Make a 'fitness profile' like Fig. 20.2 (*Introduction to Quantitative Genetics*) for human birth weight from the following data. Records of all babies born in Italy in 1974 were analysed. The data here refer to males born after a normal pregnancy of 9 months, of which there were 413,572. Birth weights were grouped in classes whose mid-points are given. The mean birth weight was 3.46 kg and the standard deviation was 0.51 kg. For each birth-weight class the mortality rate per thousand in the first four weeks, including still-births, is given. For the purpose of making the fitness profile it has to be assumed that survival to the age of four weeks is equivalent to fitness.

Birth weight, kg	Frequency, %	Mortality per 1000
1.3	0.13	612
1.8	0.34	333
2.3	2.13	94
2.8	15.95	27
3.3	40.32	15
3.8	30.73	11
4.3	8.54	12
4.8	1.56	25
5.55	0.30	69

Data from Terrenato, L. *et al.* (1981) *Ann. Hum. Genet.*, **45**, 55–63 and Ulizzi, L. *et al.* (1981) *Ann. Hum. Genet.*, **45**, 207–12.

[Solution 139]

SOLUTIONS

[Numbers in square brackets refer to the numbered equations in *Introduction to quantitative genetics*.]

1 (1.1)

(1) The total number counted is 6129. With this large number the frequencies need 5 decimal places to avoid rounding errors. The genotype frequencies are

MM: $P = 1787/6129 = 0.29156$
MN: $H = 3039/6129 = 0.49584$
NN: $Q = 1303/6129 = 0.21260$

Check that these frequencies add to 1.

(2) Putting the numbers for P, H, and Q into [1.1] gives the gene frequencies as

M: $p = [1787 + (\frac{1}{2} \times 3039)]/6129 = 0.53948$
N: $q = [1303 + (\frac{1}{2} \times 3039)]/6129 = 0.46052$

Check that $p + q = 1$.

(3) By [1.2] the expected genotype frequencies are

MM: $(0.53948)^2 = 0.29104$
MN: $2 \times 0.53948 \times 0.46052 = 0.49688$
NN: $(0.46052)^2 = 0.21208$

Check that the expected frequencies add to 1.

(4) Very close agreement. To test, we must convert the expected frequencies to expected numbers for comparison with the observed numbers. Multiplying the frequencies in (3) by the total number gives the expected numbers as

M	MN	N
1783.8	3045.4	1299.8

Check that the numbers add to 6129. χ^2 is calculated as $\Sigma[(\text{Obs.} - \text{Exp.})^2/\text{Exp.}]$, from which $\chi^2 = 0.027$. This very low value confirms the close agreement. This χ^2 has one degree of freedom because the observed numbers were used to estimate the gene frequency, and the expected numbers must be made to fit this as well as the total; in other words, there are three numbers with two constraints, so one degree of freedom is left.

2 (20.1)   The observed selection differential on bill depth (Y) was a correlated selection differential, S', following selection for fitness (W). The prediction made was $R = h^2 S'$. The response, however, is a correlated response and should be predicted from S' by [19.8b]:

$$CR_Y = \frac{r_A}{r_P} h_W h_Y S'$$

Therefore CR_Y would be correctly predicted by R if

$$\frac{r_A}{r_P} h_W h_Y = h_Y^2$$

i.e. if

$$\frac{r_A}{r_P} = \frac{h_Y}{h_W}$$

3 (3.1)   If drawn from a random-breeding population the genotypes would be in Hardy–Weinberg proportions. These, calculated as in Problem 1.1, are

aa	ab	bb	Total
101.0	821.0	1669.0	2591

The observed numbers show an excess of both homozygotes and a corresponding deficiency of heterozygotes. The discrepancy is highly significant. ($\chi_1^2 = 12.9$, $P < 0.001$.) The data suggest that the population was a mixture of sub-populations with different gene frequencies.

4 (5.1)   The following pedigree of a single first-cousin marriage will serve to illustrate all three relationships.

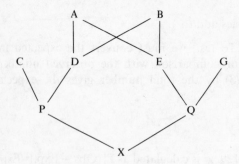

The solutions can be got in two ways, by [5.1] or by [5.2].
Applying [5.1] to the pedigree:

(1) The paths are PDAEQ and PDBEQ, giving $F_X = (\frac{1}{2})^5 + (\frac{1}{2})^5 = 1/16$.
(2) C and G are now also full sibs, so there are two more paths with $n = 5$,

giving $F_X = 4 \times (\frac{1}{2})^5 = 1/8$.

(3)   Let D be the uncle who marries his niece Q. The paths are DAEQ and DBEQ; $F = 2 \times (\frac{1}{2})^4 = 1/8$.

To apply [5.2] to (1) and (2) we need the four coancestries, CE, CG, DE, DG. With (1) all are 0 except DE which is $\frac{1}{4}$ because D and E are full sibs. $F_X = \frac{1}{4}(\frac{1}{4}) = 1/16$. With (2) CG is also $\frac{1}{4}$; $F_X = \frac{1}{4}(\frac{1}{2}) = 1/8$. With (3) the coancestries needed are AE, AG, BE, BG, of which AE and BE are $\frac{1}{4}$, being parent and offspring, and the others are 0; $F_X = 1/8$.

5 **(6.1)**   The range of values is small enough that the observations do not need to be grouped into wider classes. To construct the table, make a column of the leaf numbers in order, as under X in the table. Then go through the data making a mark for each plant against its leaf number. For ease of counting, make each fifth mark diagonally through the previous four, making a 'gate'. Finally count the marks, as under n in the table. The calculations of means and variances are shown at the foot of the table. The arithmetic is simplified if the leaf numbers are coded as deviations from 12, as shown under x. The main difference is that the F_2 is more variable.

			F_1			F_2		
X	x	x^2	n	nx	nx^2	n	nx	nx^2
12	0	0	—	—	—	1	0	0
13	1	1	1	1	1	3	3	3
14	2	4	2	4	8	5	10	20
15	3	9	7	21	63	4	12	36
16	4	16	11	44	176	3	12	48
17	5	25	1	5	25	3	15	75
18	6	36	3	18	108	2	12	72
19	7	49	—	—	—	1	7	49
20	8	64	—	—	—	2	16	128
21	9	81	—	—	—	1	9	81
Σ	—	—	25	93	381	25	96	512
Mean			15.72 ± 0.24			15.84 ± 0.49		
Variance			1.46			5.97		

$$\text{Mean} = 12 + \frac{\Sigma nx}{25} \qquad \text{Variance} = \frac{1}{24}\left[\Sigma(nx^2) - \frac{(\Sigma nx)^2}{25}\right]$$

$$\text{Standard error of mean} = \sqrt{\left[\frac{\text{variance}}{25}\right]}$$

6 (7.1)   Multiply frequency by activity, sum over genotypes, and (if percent frequencies have been used) divide by the total of 100.

	freq. × activity
AA	1171.2
AB	7438.2
BB	6448.4
AC	515.2
BC	1060.0

Mean $= \overline{16633.0}/100 = 166.33$

7 (8.1)   The first assumption is that the varieties crossed were homozygous at all loci. Tobacco is normally self-pollinating so this is likely to be true. The F_1 variance is then wholly environmental in origin. The F_2 variance is both environmental and genetic in origin. The second assumption is that the environmental variance in the F_2 is the same as that in the F_1. With this assumption the genetic variance is obtained by subtraction.

$$
\begin{aligned}
F_2 \text{ variance} &= V_G + V_E = 5.97 \\
F_1 \text{ variance} &= V_E = 1.46 \\
V_G & = 4.51
\end{aligned}
$$

Degree of genetic determination $= \dfrac{V_G}{V_G + V_E} = \dfrac{4.51}{5.97} = 0.76$, or 76 per cent.

8 (9.1)   The children are related as half sibs (see Problem 5.2) so, from Table 9.3, $r = \frac{1}{4}$.

9 (11.1)   Use Appendix Table A to get the intensity of selection, i, from the proportion selected, p. Then apply [11.3] taking σ_P as the square root of the variance. The working is as follows.

(1) (a) $R = 1.271 \times 0.37 \times 3.271 = 1.54$ g.
    (b) $R = 0.798 \times 0.37 \times 3.271 = 0.97$ g.
    (c) When p is greater than 50 per cent, take i for $1 - p$ and multiply by
        $(1 - p)/p$. $i = 1.271 \times 0.25/0.75 = 0.424$; $R = 0.51$ g.
(2) $R = 1.755 \times 0.18 \times 1.304 = 0.41$ days.
(3) Intensity of selection on females $= 1.159$. Males are not selected, so $i = \frac{1}{2} \times 1.159 = 0.5795$; $R = 0.5795 \times 0.22 \times 2.074 = 0.26$ young per litter. When selection is for fertility the offspring are already born when the individuals whose fertility has been measured are ready to be selected. An alternative way of looking at the process is to regard the offspring of both sexes as being selected on the basis of their mother's fertility. The regression of offspring on mothers is $\frac{1}{2}h^2$, so the response in this instance is $R = 1.159 \times (\frac{1}{2} \times 0.22) \times 2.074 = 0.26$ young per litter.

10   (17.1) The variances can be transformed to logarithms by [17.2] as follows.

	Small		Control		Large
C	0.143		0.111		0.128
$1+C^2$	1.0204		1.0123		1.0164
σ^2 (logs) $\times 100$	0.3809		0.2306		0.3068
σ (logs)	0.062		0.048		0.055
Mean of logs	1.074		1.362		1.597
Response in logs		0.288		0.235	

If the responses are equal when transformed to logarithms, the ratio of the arithmetic means will be equal:

$L/C = 39.85/23.16 = 1.72$
$C/S = 23.16/11.97 = 1.93$

The asymmetry is much reduced. Alternatively, the means of log-transformed data can be calculated from the formula for $(\overline{\log x})$ in [17.1]. The values are given above. The responses in log-units are nearly equal. This is to be expected from the fact that the response is proportional to the standard deviation ([11.3]), and the standard deviations of log-units are nearly equal.

11   (1.2) Non-tasters are homozygotes for the non-tasting gene. With Hardy–Weinberg frequencies, the frequency of homozygotes is the square of the gene frequency. So $q = \sqrt{(0.3)} = 0.55$.

12   (2.1)   First get the coefficient of selection, s, against white-flowered plants. The fitness relative to blue is $143/229 = 0.62$, and $s = 1 - 0.62 = 0.38$. White-flowered plants are homozygotes and their frequency is q^2, assuming random pollination. From [2.12] the mutation rate is

$u = sq^2 = 0.38 \times 7.4 \times 10^{-4} = 2.8 \times 10^{-4}$

Note that the fitness, 0.62, is that of plants as females. The calculation assumes that their fitness as males was equally reduced.

13   (3.2) Calculate the gene frequencies and Hardy–Weinberg expectations separately for each race and compare with the observed numbers. The χ^2 tests agreement between observed and expected numbers.

	p (of a)	aa	ab	bb	χ^2_1
Arctic	0.1214	18.0	260.0	941.0	1.8
Coastal	0.2649	96.3	534.3	741.4	2.2

The gene frequencies are different in the two races, so an excess of homozygotes is expected in the mixed sample. Each race has genotype frequencies in good agreement with the Hardy–Weinberg expectation for its own gene frequency.

So the subdivision into these two races, each having mated at random within the race, is sufficient to account for the genotype frequencies in the total sample.

14 (5.2)   The twins are genetically equivalent to a single individual. The two marriages are therefore equivalent to one individual with two spouses, so the children are related as half sibs and their coancestry is 1/8. (See [5.7].) If worked out from the pedigree by [5.1] the pair of twins must be shown by a single individual in the pedigree.

15 (6.2)   The data have to be grouped into classes. Grouping by 1 g intervals makes 15 classes, which is satisfactory. The classes, X, are tabulated by the integral part of the weight, i.e. ignoring the decimal part. The class intervals are 4.0–4.9, 5.0–5.9 etc., and the class mid-points are 4.45, 5.45 etc. The mean is therefore $0.45 + \overline{X}$. Different groupings will give slightly different estimates of the mean and variance.

X	4	5	6	7	8	9	10	11	12	13	14	15	16	17	18
n	1	2	5	1	0	0	1	6	4	8	10	7	2	2	1

	All	Pygmy	Normal
Mean	12.61	6.12	14.04
Variance	12.34	0.75	3.40

The distribution is bimodal, with no overlap. The 9 very small mice are clearly distinct from the others in some way. In fact, they were homozygous for a dwarfing gene called pygmy, which is used for Examples in Chapters 7 and 8. The presence of the pygmy gene greatly increases the variance.

16 (7.2)   This can be done by use of [7.2], but it is probably simpler to calculate the Hardy–Weinberg frequencies and get the mean by summing activity × frequency.

	Activity	Frequency		
		(1)	(2)	(3)
AA	122	0.04	0.25	0.64
AB	154	0.32	0.50	0.32
BB	188	0.64	0.25	0.04
Mean		174.48	154.50	134.88

17 (8.2) This only requires the substitution of α, d and q in [8.3a] and [8.4]. The values of α and d were found in solving the Chapter 7 problems.

		α	d	q	$2pq$	$V_A = 2pq\alpha^2$	$V_D = (2pqd)^2$
(1)	(1)	33.6	-1	0.2	0.32	361.27	0.10
	(2)	33.0	-1	0.5	0.50	544.50	0.25
	(3)	32.4	-1	0.8	0.32	335.92	0.10
(2)		0	50	0.4	0.48	0	576.00
(3)	Gene b:	2.5	2.5	0.5	0.50	3.125	1.56
	Gene c^e:	11.4	28.5	0.2	0.32	41.59	83.17
	Both genes:					44.71	84.74

18 (9.2) The solution to Problem 8.2 (3) gave $V_A = 44.71$ and $V_D = 84.74$, to which we have to add $V_E = \frac{1}{3}(V_A + V_D) = 43.15$. Adding the three components gives $V_P = 172.60$. From the covariances in Table 9.3 we then get

(1) Regression of offspring on mid-parent $= V_A/V_P$ $= 0.259$
(2) Regression of offspring on one parent $= \frac{1}{2}V_A/V_P$ $= 0.130$
(3) Full-sib correlation $= (\frac{1}{2}V_A + \frac{1}{4}V_D)/V_P = 0.252$
(4) Half-sib correlation $= \frac{1}{4}V_A/V_P$ $= 0.065$
(5) Double first-cousin correlation $= (\frac{1}{4}V_A + \frac{1}{16}V_D)/V_P = 0.095$

19 (11.2) For reasons to be explained in Chapters 19 and 20, this question cannot be answered without making an important assumption, namely that the cause of the selective survival was the bill depth itself and not some other character correlated with it such as, for example, wing length. The assumption seems a reasonable one in the circumstances described. With this assumption, then, the selection differential is $S = 9.96 - 9.42 = 0.54$ mm. To predict the response we need to know the heritability, which will be taken to be 0.82 from Problem 10.8. The predicted response, by [11.2], is $R = 0.82 \times 0.54 = 0.44$ mm, an increase of 5 per cent. The predicted mean in the progeny of the survivors is $9.42 + 0.44 = 9.86$ mm. The assumption made is the subject of Problem 20.1.

20 (17.2) Calculate the heterosis as the difference between the cross and the mid-parental value. Do this first for the arithmetic values given. Then convert all the arithmetic values given to logarithms and calculate the heterosis from these. The heterosis on the two scales is shown below. We cannot use [17.1] to evaluate the mean of logarithmic values because the coefficients of variation are not given, so the scale transformation has to be done less accurately by taking the logarithms of the arithmetic means given. Logarithms to base 10 are used here. Natural logarithms, $\log_e$, could equally well have been used. The relationship between the two is $\log_{10} x = 0.4343 \log_e x$.

	Arithmetic				Logarithmic		
	L	C	S		L	C	S
L	1.94	1.135	0.025	L	0.028	0.025	0.023
C	—	0.92	0.53	C	—	0.019	0.019
S	—	—	−0.07	S	—	—	−0.002

On the arithmetic scale the heterosis varies greatly according to the size of the lines crossed; it is not easy to see if crosses between size groups differ from crosses within size groups. On the logarithmic scale the heterosis is nearly the same in all crosses, both between and within size groups, except the $S \times S$ cross which is anomalous on both scales. The difference in the absolute magnitude of the heterosis on the two scales has no meaning.

21 (1.3)   For an approximate answer the working is easier if frequencies are expressed as fractions. First get the gene frequency from $q^2 = 1/20{,}000$; $q = 1/141$. Carriers are heterozygotes, with frequency

$$2q(1-q) = 2 \times \frac{1}{141} \times \frac{140}{141}$$

$$= \frac{2}{141} \text{ (approx.)}$$

$$= 1 \text{ in } 70 \text{ (approx.)}$$

22 (2.2)   Homozygotes for white will be extremely rare and can be neglected. The frequency of white-flowered plants is then the frequency of heterozygotes, H. By [2.15] the mutation rate from blue to white is $v = sH/2 = \frac{1}{2}(0.38 \times 7.4 \times 10^{-4}) = 1.4 \times 10^{-4}$.

23 (3.3) $N = 40$. By [3.7], $\Delta F = 1/80 = 0.0125$
By [3.12], $F(t=5)\ \ = 1 - (0.9875)^5\ \ = 0.061$
$F(t=10) = 1 - (0.9875)^{10} = 0.118$

24 (5.3)   First redraw the pedigree showing the paths of transmission more clearly, and put in the parents of generation I, thus:

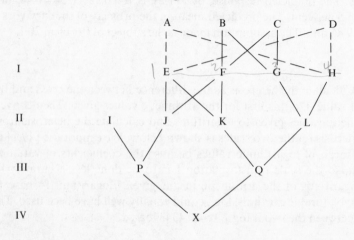

There are 6 paths, 2 through the common ancestors E and F, with $n=5$, and 4 through A, B, C, and D, all with $n=7$. None of the six common ancestors is inbred. By [5.1]

$$F_X = 2(\tfrac{1}{2})^5 + 4(\tfrac{1}{2})^2$$
$$= (\tfrac{1}{2})^4 + (\tfrac{1}{2})^5$$
$$= \tfrac{1}{16} + \tfrac{1}{32}$$
$$= \tfrac{3}{32}$$
$$= 0.09375$$

The parent, Q, is the child of a double first cousin marriage, with $F = \tfrac{1}{8}$, as seen in Problem 5.1. Note that the inbreeding of the parent does not affect the inbreeding of the children.

25 (6.3) There are 5 genotypic classes, with measurement values of -4, -3, -2, -1, 0, according to the number of loci that are homozygous for the recessive allele. The frequencies of these classes are given by the terms of the binomial expansion of $(a+b)^4$, where a is the probability of being homozygous at any particular locus. Here $a=(0.3)^2=0.09$, and $b=0.91$. The terms of the binomial expansion are

$$a^4 \qquad 4a^3b \qquad 6a^2b^2 \qquad 4ab^3 \qquad b^4$$

The coefficients, 1, 4, 6, 4, 1, are most easily got from Pascal's triangle with $n=4$, given below up to $n=6$.

n					1				
1				1		1			
2			1		2		1		
3		1		3		3		1	
4	1		4		6		4		1
5	1	5		10		10		5	1
6	1	6	15		20		15	6	1

The required frequencies, to 3 decimal places, are

Measurement class	-4	-3	-2	-1	0	Total
Frequency	0.000	0.003	0.040	0.271	0.686	1.000

The extreme asymmetry is the consequence of the low frequency of the recessive homozygotes.

26 (7.3) This can be done in three ways. (i) Calculate M from [7.2] for several different gene frequencies and graph M against q. This, of course, gives only an approximate answer.

(ii)   Treat the metric value as if it were fitness and use [2.19] to find the equilibrium gene frequency. For this we need the fitness of each homozygote relative to the heterozygote. $(1-s_1)=110/150=0.733$, $(1-s_2)=90/150=0.600$;

$s_1 = 0.267$, $s_2 = 0.400$. Then, if $\hat{q}$ is the equilibrium frequency of A_2, by [2.19] $\hat{q} = 0.267/0.667 = 0.4$.

(iii) Differentiate [7.2] with respect to q and equate to 0. (In using [7.2] care must be taken to ensure that p is the frequency of the allele that confers the higher value, in this case A_1.) Substituting $p = 1 - q$ in [7.2] and rearranging gives

$$M = a + 2(d-a)q - 2dq^2$$
$$dM/dq = 2(d-a) - 4dq$$
$$\hat{q} = \frac{d-a}{2d}$$

The mid-homozygote value is 100, and $a = 10$, $d = 50$. Thus $\hat{q} = 40/100 = 0.4$.

Substituting these values of a, d and $\hat{q}$ in [7.2] gives $M = 26$ as the deviation from the mid-homozygote value. The population mean is therefore $100 + 26 = 126$.

27 (8.3) The ratio V_D/V_G is [8.4] divided by [8.8]. Let c be the degree of dominance, so that $d = ca$. Then $2pqa^2$ cancels out and the ratio reduces to

$$\frac{V_D}{V_G} = \frac{2pqc^2}{2pqc^2 + [1 + c(q-p)]^2}$$

where q is the frequency of the recessive allele. Before working this out for different gene frequencies it is easier to substitute the value of c and then simplify further. Simplified expressions are given below, with the values of V_D/V_G for four gene frequencies. More values will have to be calculated for drawing the graphs.

	$d = \frac{1}{2}a$	$d = a$	$d = 2a$
q	$\dfrac{q - q^2}{q^2 + 3q + \frac{1}{2}}$	$\dfrac{1-q}{1+q}$	$\dfrac{q - q^2}{q^2 + \frac{1}{8}}$
0.2	0.140	0.667	0.970
0.4	0.129	0.429	0.842
0.6	0.090	0.250	0.495
0.8	0.045	0.111	0.209
Maximum	0.143	$\rightarrow 1$	1.000
at $q =$	0.250	$\rightarrow 0$	0.250

Note that most of the variance caused by a fully recessive allele at low frequency is dominance variance; but when dominance is less than complete the proportion of dominance variance is not great.

28 (9.3) The father–child and mother–child correlations are obviously consistent. To make comparisons with the midparent–child correlation we have to convert the correlations to regressions. In doing this we have to make two assumptions: that the variances in parents and in children are the same, and that the children are single children, not the means of several. With these assumptions, the regressions of children on single parents are equal to the correlations and are estimates of $\frac{1}{2}V_A/V_P$ and the estimates of V_A/V_P are 1.00 and 0.98. The midparent–child correlation estimates $(\sqrt{\frac{1}{2}})V_A/V_P$, giving $V_A/V_P = 0.69/\sqrt{\frac{1}{2}} = 0.98$. The three correlations are therefore all consistent.

29 (11.3) The intensity of selection is got from Appendix Table B; it is different in the two sexes. For males, $n=4$, $N=60$, giving $i_m = 1.882$. For females, $n=8$, $N=60$, $i_f = 1.582$. The mean (see [11.6b]) is $i = 1.732$. The predicted response per generation, from [11.3], is

$$R = 1.732 \times 0.81 \times 111 = 155.7 \text{ g}$$

The predicted mean after 5 generations is $738 + (5 \times 155.7) = 1517$ g. This prediction over 5 generations is based on the assumption that the selection does not cause a reduction of variance. In fact, with so high a heritability, there will be a substantial reduction of variance and a substantially smaller response in the generations after the first. (See Table 11.1.)

30 (17.3) Since the effect increases with the mean we might first try a log-transformation; or, more simply, look at the ratio H/L to see if it is constant. The difference between the X chromosomes after transformation to logs is given on the left below. It is a considerable improvement over the arithmetic difference, but it still increases with the mean. We therefore need a stronger transformation. This could be achieved by subtracting some constant before transformation to logs. One might guess that the 4 larger bristles should be discounted on the grounds that they are nearly invariant. The transformation would then be to $\log (x-4)$, where x is the bristle number as counted. This transformation works well, as shown below, and renders the X chromosome effect independent of the autosomal level.

| | Difference of logs | Log $(x-4)$ | | |
		High	Low	Difference
A	0.088	0.740	0.574	0.166
B	0.090	0.970	0.835	0.135
C	0.143	1.272	1.092	0.180
D	0.147	1.490	1.319	0.171
E	0.164	1.641	1.459	0.182

The required transformation can be arrived at more rationally as follows. Plot the High against the Low arithmetic values, on arithmetic paper. The points lie nearly on a straight line. We are looking for a scale on the axes which will make the line pass through the origin, i.e. zero on both axes. This will give a graph of the form $y = bx$, so that the ratio y/x is constant. If the line plotted is extended downwards it will be found to pass through, or close to, the point

$H=4$, $L=4$. This means that $(H-4)/(L-4)$ is constant, and the required transformation is $\log(x-4)$.

31   (1.4) $\dfrac{\text{Heterozygotes}}{\text{Normals}} = \dfrac{2pq}{1-q^2} = \dfrac{2q(1-q)}{(1+q)(1-q)} = \dfrac{2q}{1+q}$

Putting $\dfrac{2q}{1+q} = \tfrac{1}{3}$ gives the solution, $q = \tfrac{1}{5} = 0.2$.

(*Note*: Remember that when the gene frequencies of two alleles are written as p and q, $p+q=1$, and so $p=1-q$. In doing the algebra of gene frequencies it is usually best to substitute $p=1-q$, or $q=1-p$, as a first step).

32   (2.3)   By [2.4] the gene frequency of a will be $10^{-4}/(10^{-4}+10^{-5})=$ $1/(1+10^{-1})=10/11=0.90909$. The Hardy–Weinberg frequencies are then $AA=0.0083$, $Aa=0.1653$, $aa=0.8264$.

33   (3.4)   The expected mean is the gene frequency in the base population, i.e. 0.3. This would be found if the number of students was large.

The sample subjected to electrophoresis can be regarded as a sixth generation of parents, so that there have been six generations of random drift. First get $F(t=6)$, as in Problem 3.3, but with $N=20$. This gives $F=0.141$. Then, by [3.14], the variance of the gene frequencies would be $\sigma_q^2 = 0.3 \times 0.7 \times 0.141$ $=0.030$. The standard deviation of the students' estimates would be $\sqrt{(0.030)}$ $=0.17$.

34   (5.4)   First get the inbreeding coefficient by [5.15] as

$$F = \frac{1-0.01}{1+0.01} = 0.9802$$

Then, by [3.15], the frequency of heterozygotes relative to the Hardy–Weinberg frequency is

$$H_t/H_0 = 1 - F = 0.0198$$

The Hardy–Weinberg frequency is

$$H_0 = 2 \times 0.2 \times 0.8 = 0.32$$

The required frequency of heterozygotes in the population is therefore

$$H_t = 0.0198 \times 0.32 = 0.63 \text{ per cent.}$$

35   (6.4)   The binomial frequencies have first to be worked out for the two kinds of loci separately. In each case there are 3 genotypic classes, with binomial frequencies a^2 $2ab$ b^2, where a and b are as follows.

Loci with $q=0.3$: $a=0.09$, $b=0.91$
Loci with $q=0.7$: $a=0.49$, $b=0.51$

The binomial frequencies and genotypic classes of the two kinds of loci are shown in the margins of the following table.

	Class	Freq.	Loci with $q=0.3$		
			-2	-1	0
			0.008	0.164	0.828
			-4	-3	-2
	-2	0.240			
			0.002	0.039	0.199
Loci with $q=0.7$			-3	-2	-1
	-1	0.500			
			0.004	0.082	0.414
			-2	-1	0
	0	0.260			
			0.002	0.043	0.215

The two kinds of loci are put together in the body of the table. The genotypic class is got by adding the two marginal classes, and the frequency is got by multiplying the two marginal frequencies. There are five genotypic classes. Adding together the frequencies in the cells representing the same class gives the frequency distribution as follows.

Measurement class	-4	-3	-2	-1	0	Total
Frequency	0.002	0.043	0.283	0.457	0.215	1.000

36 (7.4) The genotypic values as defined in Fig. 7.1 are $a_b=\frac{1}{2}(95-90)=2.5$; $a_c=\frac{1}{2}(95-38)=28.5$. (Subscript c denotes the c^e gene.) In both cases $d=a$, and [7.2] then reduces to $M=a(1-2q^2)$, where q is the frequency of the recessive and reducing allele. This gives

$$M_b=2.5[1-2(0.5)^2]=1.25 \quad \text{and} \quad M_c=28.5[1-2(0.2)^2]=26.22.$$

Putting both genes together as in [7.3], $M=1.25+26.22=27.47$. This is the deviation from the mid-point of the two double homozygotes. The value of the double dominant homozygote is 95 as stated. Given that the gene effects are additive, the value of the double recessive homozygote is

$$95-2a_b-2a_c=95-5-57=33.$$

The mid-homozygote value is therefore $\frac{1}{2}(95+33)=64$. This makes the mean granule number $64+27.47=91.47$.

An alternative and quicker way to get the mean is from the values and frequencies of the four genotypes, as shown below. The values, i.e. granule numbers, entered are those given in Example 7.3.

Genotype	Freq.	B – 0.75	bb 0.25
C –	0.96	95	90
		0.72	0.24
$c^e c^e$	0.04	38	34
		0.03	0.01

Mean $= (95 \times 0.72) + (90 \times 0.24) + (38 \times 0.03) + (34 \times 0.01) = 91.48$.

37 (8.4) We have to get V_A by [8.3a] and V_D by [8.4] for each gene separately and then add them together. The genotypic values, a and d, for doing this must be taken from the means in the margins of table (ii) in the solution to Problem 7.9.

Gene b: $\quad a = d = \frac{1}{2}(0.228 + 0.342) = 0.285; \quad q = \sqrt{(0.4)} = 0.6325$
Gene c^e: $\quad a = d = \frac{1}{2}(0.060 + 0.240) = 0.150; \quad q = \sqrt{(0.2)} = 0.4472$

Gene b: $\quad \alpha = 0.285(1 + 0.6325 - 0.3675) = 0.3605$
Gene c^e: $\quad \alpha = 0.150(1 + 0.4472 - 0.5528) = 0.1342$

	$V_A = 2pq\alpha^2$	$V_D = (2pqd)^2$
Gene b	0.0604	0.0176
Gene c^e	0.0089	0.0055
Both genes	0.0693	0.0231

The interaction variance, V_I, is calculated directly from the interaction deviations in table (iv) of the solution to Problem 7.9. The values in the table are deviations from the population mean, so their variance is simply the mean of their squares. To get V_I, therefore, multiply the square of each interaction deviation by the frequency of the genotype and add:

$V_I = 0.48(0.04)^2 + 0.32(-0.06)^2 + 0.12(-0.16)^2 + 0.08(0.24)^2 = 0.0096$
$V_A = 0.0693 = 67.94\%$
$V_D = 0.0231 = 22.65\%$
$V_I = 0.0096 = 9.41\%$
$V_G = \overline{0.1020} = \overline{100.00\%}$

To check, work out V_G directly from the values in table (ii) of Problem 7.9. The variance of the additive expectations in table (iii) gives $V_A + V_D$.

38 (9.4) With standardized litters the full-sib correlation is a little higher than the daughter–dam regression. This could be due to dominance or common environment or both. The size of the litter in which a female is reared affects her own subsequent litter size for the following reason. Females reared in larger litters have to share their prenatal and pre-weaning nutrition with a larger number of competitors and they are consequently smaller at weaning and as adults. Being smaller, they ovulate fewer eggs and have smaller litters. Sibs reared as litter mates share the environment of the litter in which they were reared. The variation of litter size when litters are not standardized thus causes environmental covariance which increases the full-sib correlation, as seen in the data. The size of litter in which a female is reared is the mother's litter size. So, when litters are not standardized, mothers with larger litters tend to have daughters with smaller litters. There is therefore a negative environmental covariance of daughters' with mothers' litter sizes. This counterbalances the positive genetic covariance and the resultant daughter-dam regression is nearly zero when litters are not standardized. Note how this maternal effect causes a positive environmental covariance of litter mates but a negative environmental covariance of offspring with parents.

39 (11.4) The selection differential in each generation has first to be calculated as $S = P - M$. This is the selection to which the response is seen in the next generation. Each selection differential is therefore entered in the table against the progeny generation. Generation 0 has had no selection applied to it. The figures in the table under R, for response, are simply the generation means. Next, the selection differentials are added successively to give the cumulated selection differential as shown under ΣS. For the divergence, the values of R and ΣS in each generation are got by subtracting those of the Low line from those of the High line. The realized heritability is estimated by the regression of R on ΣS, with the values for generation 0 included. Alternatively, it can be estimated, though less reliably, as the ratio of the total response to the total selection. For the High line this is $(2.44 - 2.16)/0.45 = 0.62$.

	High			Low			Divergence	
Gen.	R	S	ΣS	R	S	ΣS	R	ΣS
0	2.16	0	0	2.16	0	0	0	0
1	2.26	0.16	0.16	2.06	-0.14	-0.14	0.20	0.30
2	2.26	0.08	0.24	2.03	-0.06	-0.20	0.23	0.44
3	2.33	0.11	0.35	2.02	-0.06	-0.26	0.31	0.61
4	2.45	0.08	0.43	2.05	-0.06	-0.32	0.40	0.75
5	2.44	0.02	0.45	2.01	-0.04	-0.36	0.43	0.81
Reg. R on ΣS		0.631			0.362			0.512
Total response / Total selection		0.62			0.42			0.53

40 (19.1) Heritability (see Table 10.4)

Weight gain:
$$h_G^2 = 4 \times \frac{1602}{12321} = 0.52$$

Food consumption:
$$h_F^2 = 4 \times \frac{6150}{61504} = 0.40$$

Phenotypic correlation: $r_P = \dfrac{22848}{\sqrt{(12321 \times 61504)}} = 0.83$

Genetic correlation: $r_A = \dfrac{2229}{\sqrt{(1602 \times 6150)}} = 0.71$

Environmental correlation:

$$r_E = \frac{22848 - (4 \times 2229)}{\sqrt{\{[12321 - (4 \times 1602)][61504 - (4 \times 6150)]\}}} = 0.94$$

Alternatively, the environmental correlation can be calculated from [19.1] for which the following are needed

h_G = 0.7211 e_G = 0.6928
h_F = 0.6325 e_F = 0.7746
$h_G h_F$ = 0.4561 $e_G e_F$ = 0.5366

Substituting into [19.1] gives

$$0.83 = (0.71 \times 0.4561) + (r_E \times 0.5366)$$
$$r_E = 0.94$$

41 (1.5) The genes can be counted and their frequencies determined by extension of [1.1].

A: $0.096 + \frac{1}{2}(0.483 + 0.028) = 0.3515$
B: $0.343 + \frac{1}{2}(0.483 + 0.050) = 0.6095$
C: $0 \quad + \frac{1}{2}(0.028 + 0.050) = 0.0390$
                    Total $\overline{1.0000}$

The Hardy–Weinberg expectation of CC is $(0.0390)^2 = 0.0015$. The expected number in a sample of 178 is 0.27. None was found because the expectation was well below 1.

42 (2.4) None. The equilibrium by [2.4] is the same when both rates are increased by the same proportion.

43 (3.5) Problem 3.4 gave $\sigma_q^2 = 0.03$. The initial gene frequencies were 0.3 and 0.7. Then by [3.5] the genotype frequencies will be

A_1A_1: $0.09 + 0.03 = 0.12$
A_1A_2: $0.42 - 0.06 = 0.36$
A_2A_2: $0.49 + 0.03 = 0.52$

44 (5.5) The solution comes from [5.15] rearranged to give C in terms of F. F is got by [3.15], but for this we need the Hardy–Weinberg frequency of heterozygotes, H_0. The gene frequencies, by [1.1] are 0.6 and 0.4. So $H_0 = 0.48$. Then, by [3.15],

$$1 - F = 0.12/0.48 = 0.25;$$
$$F = 0.75.$$

[5.15] rearranged becomes

$$C = \frac{1-F}{1+F} = \frac{0.25}{1.75} = 0.143$$

The indicated frequency of cross-pollination is 14 per cent.

45 (6.5) To get the frequencies from the binomial expansion in this case we have to work with genes, not genotypes. Because there is no dominance, the measurement is determined by the number of increasing alleles, each one adding 1 unit of measurement. With 3 loci, the genotype can have from 0 to 6 increasing alleles, making 7 classes. The frequencies are given by the expansion of $(p+q)^6$, where p and q are the gene frequencies, 0.4 and 0.6.

Measurement class	0	1	2	3	4	5	6	
Frequency	p^6	$6p^5q$	$15p^4q^2$	$20p^3q^3$	$15p^2q^4$	$6pq^5$	q^6	Total
Frequency, %	0.4	3.7	13.8	27.6	31.1	18.7	4.7	100.0

46 (7.5) It is best to get the average effect of the gene substitution, α, first from [7.5]. For this we have to evaluate a and d as defined in Fig. 7.1. Taking the values of the enzyme activities of the genotypes AA, AB and BB as given in Problem 7.1, a and d are calculated as

$$a = \tfrac{1}{2}(188 - 122) = 33$$
$$d = 154 - \tfrac{1}{2}(188 + 122) = -1$$

In reality there is probably no dominance, i.e. $d=0$, but the solution will be worked out with $d=-1$ as if it were real. The gene frequencies, q, specified in Problem 7.2 are those of allele A which is the allele conferring the lower value, and this is what is required in [7.5].

(1) $q=0.2$. Substitution into [7.5] gives

$$\alpha = 33 + [-1(0.2 - 0.8)] = 33 + 0.6 = 33.6.$$

The average effects of the alleles separately are given by [7.7]. Here α_1 refers to the allele whose frequency is p, which is B. So, from [7.7]

$$\alpha_B = 0.2 \times 33.6 = 6.72$$
$$\alpha_A = -0.8 \times 33.6 = -26.88$$

Check that $\alpha_B - \alpha_A = \alpha$.

(2) $q=0.5$: $\alpha = 33 + 0 = 33$; $\alpha_B = 16.5$; $\alpha_A = -16.5$.
(3) $q=0.8$: $\alpha = 33 - 0.6 = 32.4$; $\alpha_B = 25.92$; $\alpha_A = -6.48$

(*Note*: with strictly no dominance ($d=0$), α is equal to a and is the same for all gene frequencies, but α_A and α_B remain dependent on the gene frequency.)

47 (8.5) For (1) we need the correlation, r, between first and second litters, and for (2) we need the regression, b, of second on first, and the two means.

Let X represent first litters and Y represent second litters.

$$\begin{aligned}
\Sigma X &= 104 & \Sigma Y &= 103 \\
\Sigma X^2 &= 1106 & \Sigma Y^2 &= 1101 & \Sigma XY &= 1089 \\
\bar{X} &= 10.4 & \bar{Y} &= 10.3
\end{aligned}$$

The corrected sums of squares and products are

$$\Sigma x^2 = 24.4 \qquad \Sigma y^2 = 40.1 \qquad \Sigma xy = 17.8$$

The repeatability is estimated as the product moment correlation, which is

$$r = 17.8/\sqrt{(24.4 \times 40.1)} = 0.57$$

The estimate from this small sample is higher than would normally be found in larger samples. The repeatability could be estimated as the intraclass correlation, which works out to be 0.59, but this is not strictly valid when the variances of X and Y differ, which they do: $\sigma_X^2 = 2.7$, $\sigma_Y^2 = 4.5$.

(2)   The regression of second on first litter sizes is

$$b_{YX} = 17.8/24.4 = 0.73$$

Expected size of second litters:

   (a) $10.3 + 0.73(14 - 10.4) = 12.9$
   (b) $10.3 + 0.73(5 - 10.4) = 6.4$

These are the predicted mean sizes of the second litters of (a) all mice whose first litters were 14 and (b) all mice whose first litters were 5.

48   (10.1)   According to [10.5] the correlation or regression has to be multiplied by $1/r$, the values of r being given in Table 9.3. In the cases of (4) and (7) the factors analogous to $1/r$ are explained in the text and are shown in parentheses below.

	$1/r$	h^2
(1)	2	0.42
(2)	2	0.54
(3)	2	0.68
(4)	(1)	0.32
(5)	4	0.08
(6)	4	0.12
(7)	(2)	0.18

49   (11.5)   The unweighted selection differential is the difference between the mean of the parents and the mean of their generation; the calculation is shown in the table. Note that selection was for reduced size, so a selection differential with negative sign is what was desired. To get the weighted selection differential, calculate the weighted mean of the parents, weighting by the number of offspring. If P is the parental value and n is the corresponding number of offspring, the weighted mean is $\Sigma nP/\Sigma n$. For females this is

$$[(7.6 \times 1) + (12.4 \times 9) + \cdots]/69 = 917.6/69 = 13.30$$

The rest of the calculation is shown in the table.

	Unweighted		Weighted	
	Females	Males	Females	Males
Mean of parents (a)	12.59	13.01	13.30	13.75
Mean of parents' generation (b)	13.14	14.80	13.14	14.80
Selection differential (a–b)	−0.55	−1.79	+0.16	−1.05
Mean of sexes		−1.17		−0.445

Natural selection for fertility in females opposed the artificial selection for small size, to an extent that the effective selection differential was in the wrong direction. The similar but much smaller effect in males was probably accidental.

50 (19.2) The variances and covariance in the uniform population are environmental only. Subtraction of these from the values in the variable population estimates the genotypic variances and covariance (see Example 8.1).

Population	Cause of variation	Correlation
Variable	$G+E$	$0.87/\sqrt{(0.366 \times 43.4)} = 0.22 = r_P$
Uniform	E	$0.27/\sqrt{(0.186 \times 16.6)} = 0.15 = r_E$
V − U	G	$0.60/\sqrt{(0.180 \times 26.8)} = 0.27 = r_G$

The genetic correlation, r_G, estimated in this way is the correlation of genotypic values. The genetic correlation, r_A, in Problem 19.1 was estimated from the sire components and is the correlation of breeding values.

51 (1.6) The gene frequency in males is the frequency of affected males, given as 0.07. Under Hardy–Weinberg equilibrium the gene frequency is the same in females as in males. (1) The frequency of heterozygous women is

$$2q(1-q) = 2 \times 0.07 \times 0.93 = 0.13,$$

or 13 per cent. (2) The frequency of colour-blind (i.e. homozygous) women is $q^2 = 0.0049$, or about 1 in 200. (3) The frequency of the marriage is the product of the frequencies in men and in women, $0.07 \times 0.0049 = 0.000343$, or about 1 in 3000.

52 (2.5) The selection coefficient, originally $s = 1$, is halved by the treatment. At equilibrium, present and future, the frequency of homozygotes, by [2.13], is $q^2 = u/s$. Halving s will double the frequency of homozygotes when the new equilibrium is reached. The increase of gene frequency comes from mutation so it will take a very long time to reach the new equilibrium.

53 (3.6) The observed frequency of heterozygotes is $H_t = 0.1343$. The gene frequencies in the population as a whole, by [1.1], are 0.1413 and 0.8587. The frequency of heterozygotes in a single random-breeding population with these gene frequencies is $H_0 = 0.2427$. The panmictic index, by [3.15], is

$$P = \frac{0.1343}{0.2427} = 0.553$$

and the coefficient of inbreeding is

$$F = 0.447$$

54 (5.6) A double first-cousin mating produces an inbreeding coefficient of $F = 0.125$ (Problem 5.1). Three generations of full-sib mating produce $F = 0.5$ (Table 5.1) relative to generation 1 as base. Then, by [5.17], the final inbreeding coefficient relative to generation 0 as base is

$$1 - F = (1 - 0.125)(1 - 0.5) = 0.4375$$
$$F = 0.5625$$

55 (6.6) A symmetrical distribution results when $a = b = \frac{1}{2}$ in $(a+b)^n$. (1) With recessives, $a = q^2$, where q is the frequency of the recessive alleles; $q = \sqrt{\frac{1}{2}} = 0.707$. (2) With no dominance, $a = q$; $q = 0.5$.

56 (7.6) The breeding values are obtained from Table 7.3 where A_1A_1 corresponds with BB. The values of α needed were found in Problem 7.5.

		(1) $q = 0.2$ $\alpha = 33.6$	(2) $q = 0.5$ $\alpha = 33.0$	(3) $q = 0.8$ $\alpha = 32.4$
BB	$2q\alpha$	13.44	33	51.84
AB	$(q-p)\alpha$	−20.16	0	19.44
AA	$-2p\alpha$	−53.76	−33	−12.96

These values are deviations from the population mean. Check that the mean breeding value is zero in each population: multiply the breeding value by the genotype frequency (Hardy–Weinberg) in that population and sum over genotypes.

57 (8.6) (1) The mean square for litter order is not relevant except to show that the variance between litters of different order (first, second, etc.) has been removed from the within-sow variance, i.e. from V_{Ew}. The repeatability is given by the intraclass correlation, $r = \sigma_b^2 / (\sigma_b^2 + \sigma_w^2)$, where σ_b^2 is the component between sows and σ_w^2 is the component within sows. The mean square within sows is σ_w^2. The mean square between sows is composed of $\sigma_w^2 + 10\sigma_b^2$. (The 10 is because each sow had 10 litters.) Thus

$$\sigma_b^2 = (25.56 - 3.23)/10 = 2.233$$
$$r = 2.233/(2.233 + 3.23) = 0.409$$

Estimation of the repeatability by the intraclass correlation assumes that the variances do not differ in successive litters.

(2) Basing the measure on the mean of more than one litter reduces V_P (see [8.14]), and the relative reduction is given by [8.15]. V_A is unchanged. The heritability when only one litter is used is V_A/V_P, and when n litters are used it is $V_A/V_{P(n)}$. The heritability with n litters relative to the heritability with one litter is therefore $V_P/V_{P(n)}$, which is simply the reciprocal of [8.15].

n	$V_{P(n)}/V_P$	h_n^2/h^2
2	0.704	1.42
3	0.606	1.65
4	0.557	1.80

Taking two litters would increase the heritability by 42 per cent, and taking four litters by 80 per cent.

58 (10.2) The inconsistency between sons and daughters is removed if correction is made for the difference in variance between males and females. The correction factors, by which the regressions and their standard errors are to be multiplied, are: for daughter–father, $\sigma_m/\sigma_f = 2.5/2.3 = 1.087$; for son–mother, $\sigma_f/\sigma_m = 0.920$. The estimates of the heritability, obtained by making this correction and then doubling the regression and its standard error, are as follows.

	Father	Mother
Sons	0.646 ± 0.116	0.835 ± 0.105
Daughters	0.633 ± 0.096	0.840 ± 0.096
Mean	0.64 ± 0.075	0.84 ± 0.071

The estimates from mothers are substantially higher than those from fathers, which can be attributed to a maternal effect. Consequently the regressions on mid-parent are not useful, and the regressions on fathers provide the most reliable estimates. There are no reasons to prefer the sons or the daughters, so we take the mean as $h^2 = 0.64 \pm 0.075$. The standard error is obtained as $\frac{1}{2}\sqrt{[(0.116)^2 + (0.096)^2]}$.

Now consider the regressions on mothers. By doubling the regression, as in the table, we have also doubled the covariance due to the maternal effect. Therefore $\frac{1}{2}(0.84 - 0.64) = 0.10$ estimates the environmental covariance of mothers and their children, expressed as a proportion of V_P.

59 (11.6) On average, 2 lambs from each ewe must be selected in order to replace the parents. After one breeding season there are not enough lambs to provide replacements, so the parents must be kept for at least 2 seasons. After 2 breeding seasons each ewe has on average 2.4 lambs; selecting 2 out of 2.4 ($p = 83$ per cent) makes $i = 0.305$ (from Appendix Table A because the numbers are large.) The generation interval is the mean age of the parents at the birth of their selected offspring, which in this case is 2.5 years. The intensity of selection per year is then 0.122. The table shows this calculation for each year of age at which the parents might be discarded, up to 7. The intensity of selection per year is maximal when the parents have bred for 5 seasons and are 6 years old. The parents should therefore be discarded after their 5th breeding season. The The portion selected in each year will then be 1 out of 3 for the following reason. Each year 1 out of 5 pairs are replaced, having produced on average 1.2 lambs in that year. The proportion of the total lambs needed to replace them is therefore

$$\frac{1}{5} \times \frac{2}{1.2} = \frac{1}{3}.$$

Or, when due for replacement each pair has produced on average a total of 6 lambs. So to replace each pair, $2/6 = 1/3$ must be selected.

Age of parents when discarded	Generation interval (L)	Total lambs per ewe (N)	$p = 2/N$ %	i	i/L
3	2.5	2.4	83	0.305	0.122
4	3.0	3.6	56	0.704	0.235
5	3.5	4.8	42	0.931	0.266
6	4.0	6.0	33	1.097	0.274
7	4.5	7.2	28	1.202	0.267

60 (19.3)   Taking the intensity of selection from Appendix Table A gives

Males: $i = 1.755$
Females: $i = 1.400$
Mean: $i = 1.5775$

The direct responses are predicted by [11.3] and the correlated responses by [19.6]. The data needed from Problem 19.1 are

$h_G^2 = 0.52$ $h_F^2 = 0.40$ $r_A = 0.71$
$\sigma_G = 111$ g $\sigma_F = 248$ g

giving, for substitution into [19.6], $h_G h_F r_A = 0.324$.

Response of weight gain
Direct: $R = 1.5775 \times 0.52 \times 111 = 91.1$ g
Correlated: $CR = 1.5775 \times 0.324 \times 111 = 56.7$ g

Response of food consumption
Direct: $R = 1.5775 \times 0.40 \times 248 = 156.5$ g
Correlated: $CR = 1.5775 \times 0.324 \times 248 = 126.8$ g

61 (1.7)   The gene frequency in the parents is known and should be used to calculate the expectations. The frequency of *so* was $8/40 = 0.2$. The Hardy–Weinberg genotype frequencies in the progeny are, by [1.2], 0.04, 0.32, 0.64. Multiplying these by the total number counted, 1441, gives the expected numbers (to the nearest whole number) as

so/so	so/cn	cn/cn
58	461	922

There was an excess of homozygotes and a corresponding deficiency of hetero-zygotes. Possible reason: assortative mating due to some of the female parents having mated with their own stock males before being put in the vials. The discrepancy is highly significant, with $\chi^2 = 125$. This χ^2 has two degrees of freedom because the observed numbers of progeny were not used to estimate the gene frequency, the only constraint being that the expected numbers must add to the observed total.

62 (2.6) $q_0^2 = 1/2500 = 0.0004$, $q_0 = 0.02$. By [2.12] the original mutation rate is $u_0 = sq_0^2$, and with $s = 1$, $u_0 = q_0^2$. The change of gene frequency from mutation is given by [2.3] and from selection, approximately, by [2.8]. Putting u_1 for the new mutation rate, the net change is

$$\Delta q = u_1(1 - q_0) - sq_0^2(1 - q_0)$$
$$= (u_1 - sq_0^2)(1 - q_0)$$

Substituting $sq_0^2 = u_0$

$$\Delta q = (u_1 - u_0)(1 - q_0)$$

Putting $u_1 = 2u_0$, and substituting $u_0 = q_0^2$

$$\Delta q = q_0^2(1 - q_0)$$
$$= 0.0004 \times 0.98$$
$$= 0.000392$$
$$q_1 = q_0 + \Delta q$$
$$= 0.020392$$
$$q_1^2 = 0.0004158 \text{ or 1 in 2405}$$

The incidence would be increased by 4 per cent of its original level. There would be 16 additional cases per million births.

63 (3.7) (1) The gene frequencies in the sample are 0.6 and 0.4, from which the Hardy–Weinberg frequency of heterozygotes is 0.48. The observed frequency is in excess of the expectation, suggesting some form of selection against one or both homozygotes. (2) With the sample coming from so few parents, chance differences of gene frequency between male and female parents become im-portant. Here $N = 8$, and the expected frequency of heterozygotes, by [3.16], is

$$H = 0.48(1 + 1/16) = 0.51.$$

This is close to the observed frequency and so the evidence for selection dis-appears.

64 (5.7) This can be worked out by pedigree analysis, using [5.1], or by coancestries, using the rule in [5.3]. But it is simpler to get the inbreeding co-efficient directly from the frequency of homozygotes. This gives the inbreeding coefficient by definition, because the genes come from highly inbred lines and all homozygotes must therefore be homozygous for alleles that are identical by descent. Call the inbred lines A and B. The F_2 individuals, taken all together, produce A and B gametes in equal proportions, as do the F_1. So the backcross to the F_1 produces $\frac{1}{4}AA + \frac{1}{4}BB$, and the backcross to A produces $\frac{1}{2}AA$. Both therefore produce 50 per cent of homozygotes and the inbreeding coefficient of both progenies is 0.5.

65 (20.2)   Let Y denote IQ score and W denote fitness as measured by family size. The change in IQ score is predicted by [20.5b]:

$$CR_Y = r_A h_Y h_W \sigma_Y \sigma_W$$

Taking h_W^2 to be 0.1 gives

$$CR_Y = 0.11 \times \sqrt{(0.6 \times 0.1)} \times 15.4 \times 2.3$$
$$= 0.95$$

Taking h_W^2 to be 0.2 gives $CR_Y = 1.35$. The predicted change is an increase of about one IQ point per generation.

The correlated selection differential is given by [20.4] as the phenotypic covariance:

$$S' = cov_P = r_P \sigma_Y \sigma_W$$
$$= 0.11 \times 15.4 \times 2.3$$
$$= 3.9 \text{ IQ points}$$

66 (7.7)   The breeding values and dominance deviations are given in Table 7.3. In solving Problem 7.3 we found $a = 10$, $d = 50$, $q = 0.4$. (q is the frequency of the reducing allele as required.) The average effect of the gene substitution must first be found from [7.5]. This is

$$\alpha = 10 + 50(0.4 - 0.6) = 0$$

All the breeding values are therefore zero. (The reason for this is that the population is at its maximum mean value, which would be its equilibrium if the character were fitness.) Substitution of p, q, and d gives the dominance deviations as

A_1A_1	A_1A_2	A_2A_2
-16	$+24$	-36

Check by seeing that the mean dominance deivation of individuals in the population is zero.

67 (12.1)   The calculations are shown in the table. The following explanations may be needed.

$\sigma_A = h\sigma_P = \sqrt{(0.2)} \times 2.10 = 0.94$

Total response at the limit (one-way), $R = 23.55 - 11.90 = 11.65$.

Half-life: This can be deduced as follows. Half the total response is 5.8. Given $S = 2.25$ and $h^2 = 0.2$, the response per generation by [11.2] is $2.25 \times 0.2 = 0.45$. Given that the response was linear, the number of generations required to give the response of 5.8 is $5.8/0.45 = 13$. This estimates the half-life.

Theoretical maximum response, by [12.2] noting that $i\sigma_P =$ selection differential $= 2.25$, $R_{(max)} = 2 \times 33 \times 0.2 \times 2.25 = 29.70$.

Theoeretical maximum half-life, assuming all genes to be additive, is $1.4 N_e = 46$.

The number of loci and their standardized effects (n and $2a/\sigma_P$) cannot be calculated without knowing the lower selection limit. One might guess that downward and upward selection would have produced equal responses, making the total range $R = 23.3$; the figures in parenthesis are based on this assumption. The assumption, however, makes the growth at the lower limit improbably small, i.e. $11.90 - 11.65 = 0.25$ g. A more reasonable guess would be that downward and upward selection would have produced the same proportional change; upward selection doubled the growth, so downward selection would have halved the growth, making the lower limit 5.95 and the total range $R = 17.6$. The first entered figures are based on this assumption. Remember, however, that estimates of gene numbers depend on several other assumptions that are unlikely to be true.

One-way response, $H/C = 23.55/11.90$		$= 2.0$
$R/\sigma_A = 11.65/0.94$		$= 12.4$
$R/\sigma_P = 11.65/2.10$		$= 5.5$
$R_{(max)}/\sigma_P$ $= 29.70/2.10$		$= 14.1$
N_e (given)		$= 33$
Duration (given)		$= 34$
Half-life (deduced)		$= 13$
Half-life$/N_e$ $= 13/33$		$= 0.39$
$\dfrac{\text{Observed}}{\text{Maximum}}$: Response $= 11.65/29.70$		$= 0.39$
Half-life $= 13/46$		$= 0.28$
No. of 'loci' [12.1]: $n = \dfrac{(17.6)^2}{8 \times (0.94)^2}$		$= 44$ (77)
$2a/\sigma_P$ (see p. 202) $= 2h\sqrt{(2/n)}$		$= 0.19$ (0.14)

68   (10.3)   Since we are working with correlations and not covariances the components will all be proportions of the total phenotypic variance V_P. The paternal half sibs give an estimate of

$$V_A/V_P = 4 \times 0.140 = 0.560.$$

In view of the standard errors this is not inconsistent with the estimate from the regression of children on fathers in Problem 10.2. The environmental variance common to children of the same mother is estimated from the difference between the maternal and paternal half-sib correlations:

$$V_{Ec}/V_P = 0.257 - 0.140 = 0.117.$$

Environmental resemblance between children of the same mother is to be expected in consequence of the environmental resemblance between children and mothers found in Problem 10.2. The two covariances are nearly the same, though this is not a necessary part of the expectation. The full-sib correlation estimates $(\frac{1}{2}V_A + \frac{1}{4}V_D + V_{Ec})/V_P$, so

$$\frac{1}{4}V_D/V_P = 0.406 - 2(0.140) - 0.117 = 0.009$$
$$V_D/V_P = 0.036$$

That this is not significantly different from zero can easily be seen without working out its standard error. The remaining component, environmental variance within sibships, is got by the difference from the total of 1. The full partitioning, in percentages, is

$$V_A + V_D + V_{Ec} + V_{Ew} = V_P$$
$$56 + 4 + 12 + 28 = 100$$

69 (14.1) The change of mean is given by [14.4] as $-2F\Sigma dpq$. After one generation of selfing $F = 0.5$ (Table 5.1), so the inbreeding depression due to the four loci is Σdpq, where d is the difference between the heterozygote value and the mid-homozygote value (Fig. 7.1). The mid-homozygote value is given below as the difference from the 'AA' value, and is one half of the 'aa' value in the table of data.

Locus	Mid-hom. value	d	pq	dpq
(1)	-10	0	0.25	0
(2)	-15	$+20$	0.25	5
(3)	-15	-5	0.16	-0.8
(4)	-30	$+30$	0.09	2.7
			Σdpq =	6.9

There would be a reduction in yield of 6.9 g due to these loci.

70 (19.4) The realized heritabilities, by [11.7], are as follows.

$$h_G^2 = 186/574 = 0.32$$
$$h_F^2 = 525/1312 = 0.40$$

The genetic correlation, by [19.7], is

$$r_A^2 = \frac{120}{186} \times \frac{412}{525} = 0.5063$$
$$r_A = \pm 0.71$$

Because the direct and correlated responses are in the same direction the sign of r_A must be positive, so $r_A = +0.71$.

71 (1.8) Hardy–Weinberg frequencies are not expected because the gene frequency was different in the male and female parents. The gene frequency of so in males was $16/20 = 0.8$, and in females $4/20 = 0.2$. Putting these as the gametic frequencies in Table 1.2 gives the genotype frequencies in the progeny as

so/so	so/cn	cn/cn
0.16	0.68	0.16

With a gene frequency of 0.5 the Hardy–Weinberg expectations are 0.25, 0.50, 0.25. Note the excess of heterozygotes resulting from the unequal gene frequencies in male and female parents.

72 (2.7) Let q be the frequency of the mutant allele, so that $q_0 = 1$. Let m be the proportion of immigrants ($m = 0.01$) with $q_m = 0$. Then [2.1] gives

$$
\begin{aligned}
q_1 &= mq_m + (1-m)q_0 \\
&= (0.01 \times 0) + (0.99 \times 1) = 0.99 \\
q_2 &= (0.01 \times 0) + (0.99 \times 0.99) = (0.99)^2 \\
q_{10} &= (0.99)^{10} = 0.9044
\end{aligned}
$$

Frequency of wild-type allele $= p = 1 - 0.9044 = 0.0956$.

After the last immigrants have bred the genotypes will be in Hardy–Weinberg proportions. Therefore

(1) Frequency of wild-type flies $= p^2 = (0.0956)^2 = 0.0091$
(2) Frequency of mutant phenotype $= 1 - p^2 = 0.9909$
   Frequency of heterozygotes $= 2pq = 0.1729$
   Frequency of heterozygotes among mutants $= 0.1729/0.9909 = 0.1745$

73 (3.8) Start from the expected frequency of heterozygotes, given as

$$
H = 2pq + \tfrac{1}{2}\overline{D^2} = 2pq + \tfrac{1}{2}\sigma_D^2
$$

where D is the difference of gene frequency between the male and female parents. Let there be M male and F female parents, with $2M$ and $2F$ genes sampled. The binomial sampling variances of the gene frequencies are $pq/2M$ in male parents, and $pq/2F$ in female parents, where p and q are the overall gene frequencies in the whole population. The sampling variance of the difference of gene frequency is

$$
\sigma_D^2 = pq/2M + pq/2F
$$

The modified equation is therefore

$$
\begin{aligned}
H &= 2pq + pq\left(\frac{1}{4M} + \frac{1}{4F}\right) \\
&= 2pq\left[1 + \left(\frac{1}{8M} + \frac{1}{8F}\right)\right]
\end{aligned}
$$

74 (5.8) Think of the part of the population made up only of cousin marriages. This is a subdivided population with $F = 1/16$. (See Problem 5.1.) The risk to the children is the frequency of homozygotes, given in Table 3.1 as $q^2 + pqF$. Call this risk Q. To evaluate Q we need the gene frequency, q. Since most marriages in the whole population are non-consanguineous we can take q to be approximately the square root of the incidence. (There is a small error in doing this because, with some cousin marriages, the genotypes are not quite in Hardy–Weinberg proportions; see Problem 5.9). Finally, the risk to the children of cousin marriages relative to the population as a whole is $R=Q/I$, where I is the population incidence.

	(1) Cystic fibrosis	(2) PKU
Incidence, $I(=q^2)$	4×10^{-4}	90.91×10^{-6}
$q=\sqrt{I}$	2×10^{-2}	9.53×10^{-3}
Fpq	12.25×10^{-4}	590×10^{-6}
$Q=q^2+Fpq$	16.25×10^{-4}	681×10^{-6}
$R=Q/I$	4.1	7.5

The risk is increased 4-fold for cystic fibrosis and $7\frac{1}{2}$-fold for PKU, but in absolute terms the risks are still small.

75 (15.1) $V_P=4.0$; $V_G=V_A=0.52\times4.0=2.08$; $V_E=4.0-2.08=1.92$. Table 15.1 gives the amount of genetic variance between and within lines.

F (Tab. 5.1)	Between lines $2FV_G$	Within lines $(1-F)V_G+V_E$	Total
(1) 0.25	1.04	3.48	4.52
(2) 0.50	2.08	2.96	5.04
(3) 0.95	3.95	2.02	5.97

At $F=0.95$ the total genetic variance (all additive) is $5.97-1.92=4.05$. Heritability $=4.05/5.97=0.68$.

76 (7.8) The relevant values found for the two genes were

Gene b: $a=d=2.5$; $q=0.5$
Gene c^e: $a=d=28.5$; $q=0.2$

First get the average effect of each gene substitution from [7.5]:

Gene b: $\alpha=2.5+2.5(0.5-0.5)=2.5$
Gene c^e: $\alpha=28.5+28.5(0.2-0.8)=11.4$

The genotype we are concerned with corresponds to A_2A_2 in Table 7.3. Substituting the above values for each locus separately gives the following.

	Breeding value $= -2p\alpha$	Dominance deviation $= -2p^2d$
Gene b:	$-2\times0.5\times2.5 = -2.50$	$-2\times(0.5)^2\times2.5 = -1.25$
Gene c^e:	$-2\times0.8\times11.4=-18.24$	$-2\times(0.8)^2\times28.5=-36.48$
Both genes:	-20.74	-37.73

Adding the breeding values of the separate loci gives the breeding value of the joint genotype; similarly for the dominance deviation. The breeding value calculated is the deviation from the population mean, which was found to be 91.47 granules. In absolute units, therefore, the breeding value is 91.47 − 20.74 = 70.73 granules.

77 (13.1)   The heritabilities are calculated by [13.4] and [13.5], given also in Table 13.4. The relative responses are calculated from the expressions in the right-hand column of Table 13.4.

	h_f^2 [13.4]	h_w^2 [13.5]	R_f/R	R_w/R
(1)	0.265	0.077	0.93	0.72
(2)	0.390	0.077	1.06	0.74
(3)	0.100	0.100	0.79	0.61
(4)	0.147	0.500	0.68	0.97
(5)	0.136	0.500	0.62	1.05

Note that, as can readily be seen from [13.4] and [13.5], when $t = r$, $h_f^2 = h^2 = h_w^2$. In these circumstances individual selection gives the best weighting of the individual and the family mean. Note also the circumstances that make family selection or within-family selection better than individual selection.

78 (10.4)   The expectations of the mean squares are

$$B = \sigma_W^2 + 2\sigma_B^2$$
$$W = \sigma_W^2$$

from which

$$\sigma_B^2 = (B - W)/2$$
$$\sigma_W^2 = W$$

The intraclass correlation is

$$t = \sigma_B^2/(\sigma_B^2 + \sigma_W^2)$$

$$= \frac{\frac{1}{2}(B - W)}{\frac{1}{2}(B - W) + W}$$

$$= \frac{B - W}{B + W}$$

79 (14.2)   The population mean, by [7.3], is $M = \Sigma a(p - q) + 2\Sigma dpq$. This is a deviation from the multiple mid-homozygote value. The mean with the favourable alleles all homozygous will be Σa, also a deviation from the multiple mid-homozygote value. Therefore the increase will be

$$\Sigma a - M$$
$$= \Sigma a - \Sigma a(p - q) - 2\Sigma dpq$$
$$= \Sigma[a(2q)] - 2\Sigma dpq$$
$$= 2(\Sigma aq - \Sigma dpq)$$

We need to know the value of a for each locus. This is half the difference between the homozygote values. The value of Σdpq was obtained in Problem 14.1 as 6.9.

Locus	a	aq
(1)	10	5
(2)	15	7.5
(3)	15	3
(4)	30	3
Σaq =		18.5

Increase $= 2(18.5 - 6.9) = 23.2$ g.

80 (19.5)   The solution comes from [19.9] with selection for body weight giving the correlated response of litter size. The intensities of selection corresponding to the proportions selected, from Appendix Table A, are

	Selection for	
	Litter size (X)	Body weight (Y)
i on females	1.271	1.271
i on males	0	1.755
i (mean)	0.6355	1.513

Substitution into [19.9] gives

$$\frac{CR}{R} = 0.43 \times \frac{1.513}{0.6355} \times \sqrt{\left(\frac{0.35}{0.22}\right)}$$
$$= 1.29$$

Selection for body weight is expected to be 29 per cent more effective than selection for litter size, mainly because males can be selected.

81 (1.9)   It can easily be shown to be true by 'trial and error' with a small number of alleles. (Calculate the frequency of heterozygotes with three alleles all at the same frequency; then recalculate with unequal frequencies.) A simple general proof comes from consideration of the variance of the allele frequencies. With equal frequencies the variance is zero. Let n be the number of alleles and q the frequency of any allele. Then $\Sigma q = 1$ and $(\Sigma q)^2 = 1$. The frequency of homozygotes is Σq^2, and when this is minimal the frequency of heterozygotes is maximal. The variance of q is given by

$$\sigma_q^2 = \frac{1}{n}\left[\Sigma q^2 - \frac{(\Sigma q)^2}{n}\right] = \frac{1}{n}\left[\Sigma q^2 - \frac{1}{n}\right]$$

Rearrangement leads to

$$\Sigma q^2 = n\sigma_q^2 + \frac{1}{n}$$

Therefore, with any value of n, the frequency of homozygotes is minimal when $\sigma_q^2 = 0$. All alleles then have equal frequencies of $1/n$.

Substituting $\sigma_q^2 = 0$ into the above equation gives the frequency of homozygotes as $1/n$. Therefore the frequency of heterozygotes is $1 - (1/n)$.

Note that the first equation above can be written in the following useful form:

$$\sigma_q^2 = \frac{\Sigma q^2}{n} - \left(\frac{\Sigma q}{n}\right)^2 = \overline{q^2} - (\overline{q})^2$$

i.e. variance = (mean of squares) − (square of mean). This is used in later chapters.

82 (2.8) Because both populations reached the same, intermediate, gene frequency selection must have favoured heterozygotes. This is to be expected because the 'heterozygotes', $so+/+cn$, are wild-type and both homozygotes are mutant. The relative magnitude of the selection coefficients against the two homozygotes can be found by [2.18]:

$$\frac{s_{(so)}}{s_{(cn)}} = \frac{p_{(cn)}}{q_{(so)}} = \frac{0.65}{0.35} = 1.86$$

83 (4.1) The effective population size is given by [4.4]. Then get ΔF by [4.1] and the inbreeding coefficient by [3.12].

No. of females	10	10	10	10
No. of males	10	5	2	1
N_e	20	13.33	6.67	3.636
ΔF		0.025	0.0375	0.075	0.1375
$F(t = 10)$	0.224	0.318	0.541	0.772

84 (5.9) The incidence in the non-inbred individuals is q^2, and in the inbred individuals is $q^2(1 - F) + qF$, from the right-hand side of Table 3.1. The overall incidence is therefore

$$I = (1 - y)q^2 + y[q^2(1 - F) + qF]$$

By multiplying out the brackets this reduces easily to

$$(1 - yF)q^2 + yFq = I$$

which can be solved for q if y and F are known.

Note that yF is the average inbreeding coefficient in the population as a whole, and the expression for the overall incidence can be got immediately from Table 3.1 by putting yF in place of F.

The equation can be used to get the exact solution to Problem 5.8, assuming there are no other causes of departure from Hardy–Weinberg proportions. The frequency of cousin marriages varies a lot, but is about 1 per cent in many populations.

85 (15.2) The components of variance between lines, from the solution of Problem 15.1, are shown on the left below. The component between lines is the variance of the true means of lines and is all genetic; the component within lines contains an environmental component of 1.92. We need to know the variance of the observed means estimated from 4 individuals, which is $\sigma_b^2 + \frac{1}{4}\sigma_w^2$ (Table 13.3). Applying this to the genetic and phenotypic components gives the variances on the right below.

	Components		Variance of observed means	
	Genetic	Phenotypic	Genetic	Phenotypic
Between lines, σ_b^2	2.08	2.08	2.34	2.82
Within lines, σ_w^2	1.04	2.96	—	—

The heritability of line means is $2.34/2.82 = 0.83$. The intensity of selection for $p = 5$ per cent is $i = 2.063$ from Appendix Table A. The expected response is given by [13.2], the lines being equivalent to families. It is

$$R = 2.063 \times 0.83 \times \sqrt{(2.82)} = 2.9 \text{ bristles}$$

86 (7.9) To get the population mean we need the frequencies of the four genotypes as shown in table (i). Multiply the value of each genotype in Example 7.7 by its frequency and add to give the population mean $= 1.112$. Convert the values to deviations from the mean as in table (ii). These deviations from the mean will now be referred to simply as values. Next, we have to look at each locus separately and find the mean value of each of its two genotypes in this population. These are given in the margins of table (ii); for example, the mean value of the C$-$ genotype is $0.6(0.328) + 0.4(-0.342) = +0.060$. Now get the additive expectations of the combined genotypes as in table (iii). These are the values the combined genotypes would have if the values of the two single-locus genotypes were simply added together. For example, the expectation for the B$-$C$-$ genotype is 0.228 (for B$-$) $+ 0.060$ (for C$-$) $= 0.288$. Finally, the inter-action deviation of each genotype is the difference between the observed value in table (ii) and the additive expectation in table (iii). These are given in table (iv). For example, the interaction deviation of B$-$ C$-$ is $0.328 - 0.288 = +0.04$. To check, see that the mean interaction deviation is zero.

(i) Frequencies

		B$-$	bb
	Freq.	0.6	0.4
C$-$	0.8	0.48	0.32
$c^e c^e$	0.2	0.12	0.08

(ii) Observed deviations from mean

	Freq.	B$-$ 0.6	bb 0.4	Mean
C$-$	0.8	0.328	-0.342	$+0.060$
$c^e c^e$	0.2	-0.172	-0.342	-0.240
Mean		$+0.228$	-0.342	0.000

(iii) Additive expectations

	B −	bb
C −	+0.288	−0.282
$c^e c^e$	−0.012	−0.582

(iv) Interaction deviations

	B −	bb
C −	+0.04	−0.06
$c^e c^e$	−0.16	+0.24

The interaction deviations can also be calculated directly from the table of genotypic values as follows. The means in the margins are obtained as in table (ii) above.

	B −	bb	Mean
C −	1.44	0.77	1.172
$c^e c^e$	0.94	0.77	0.872
Mean	1.34	0.77	1.112

Then the interaction deviation of the B − C − genotype, for example, is

$$1.44 - 1.172 - 1.34 + 1.112 = +0.04$$

87 (13.2) The responses relative to individual selection, R, are got from the expressions at the right-hand side of Table 13.4. (1) and (2) are family selection; (3) is sib selection; (4) is within-family selection.

(1) $R_f/R = \dfrac{1 + (4 \times 0.25)}{\sqrt{\{5[1 + (4 \times 0.10)]\}}} = 0.76$

(2) $R_f/R = \dfrac{1 + (4 \times 0.5)}{\sqrt{\{5[1 + (4 \times 0.36)]\}}} = 0.86$

(3) $R_s/R = \dfrac{5 \times 0.5}{\sqrt{\{5[1 + (4 \times 0.36)]\}}} = 0.72$

(4) $R_w/R = (1 - 0.5)\sqrt{\left[\dfrac{4}{5(1 - 0.36)}\right]} = 0.56$

88 (10.5) This illustrates some of the difficulties in interpreting twin data. The heritability can be estimated in three ways with different biasses, as shown in the table below. All are biassed, but in different amounts, by dominance and by epistatic components not shown in the table. (2) and (3) are biassed by common environment. The children under 10 make reasonably good sense. The degree of genetic determination is estimated approximately by (1) as 52 per cent. There is resemblance due to common environment, which can be estimated approximately by subtracting (1) from (2), or equivalently by subtracting (2) from (3), as $V_{Ec} = 12$ per cent. The children aged 10–15 do not make good sense.

It appears that V_{Ec} does not contribute to their resemblance because (2) and (3) are less than (1).

		Under 10	10–15
(1) $2(MZ-DZ)=(V_A+1\frac{1}{2}V_D)/V_P$		0.52	0.98
(2) MZ $\quad=(V_A+V_D+V_{Ec})/V_P$		0.64	0.91
(3) 2 DZ $\quad=(V_A+\frac{1}{2}V_D+2V_{Ec})/V_P$		0.76	0.84

89 (14.3)   The experiment gave two values, 8.1 and 8.5, for the mean with $F=0$. The solution will be based on the mean of these, i.e. 8.3. Let D_M and D_L be the depression due to inbreeding in the mothers and the litters respectively when $F=1$. Then from the third line of the table in Example 14.2.

$$0.5\,D_M=8.3-6.2$$
$$D_M=4.2$$

From the second line of the table

$$0.5\,D_L+0.375\,D_M=8.3-5.7$$
$$D_L=2.05$$

Inbreeding in the mothers caused about twice as much depression as inbreeding in the litters. The total depression at $F=1$ would be

$$D_M+D_L=4.2+2.05=6.25$$

and the mean litter size would be $8.3-6.25=2.05$ young per litter.

90 (19.6)   First work out the expected response to selection of females only, which was not calculated in the solution to Problem 19.5. We can assume that 25 per cent are selected out of a large number, so the intensity of selection is taken from Appendix Table A. By [11.3] the response is

$$R=\tfrac{1}{2}\times 1.271\times 0.22\times \sigma_P=0.140\ \sigma_P$$

For the joint selection we calculate the response expected from the direct selection for litter size in females by [11.3] and the correlated response from selection for body weight in males by [19.6], and then add the two expected responses together. This is equivalent to calculating the mean breeding value for litter size of the selected females and males. The units throughout are phenotypic standard deviations of litter size. The intensity of selection on females has to be taken from Appendix Table B because all are selected from small samples, i.e. 1 out of 4. The predicted responses are

From females:	$R\ =\tfrac{1}{2}\times 1.029\times 0.22$	$=0.113\ \sigma_P$
From males:	$CR=\tfrac{1}{2}\times 1.271\times \sqrt{(0.35\times 0.22)}\times 0.43=0.076\ \sigma_P$	
From both:	Joint response	$=0.189\ \sigma_P$

The joint response relative to the response expected from selecting females only is

$$\frac{0.189}{0.140} = 1.35$$

The third procedure would be 35 per cent better than the first.

91 (1.10)   The working comes from Table 1.5 and equation [1.5]. AA bb is produced by union of two recombinant gametes of type Ab, whose frequency, s, we therefore have to find. (Ab corresponds to A_1B_2 in Table 1.5). We need to know the following quantities. (i) The gene frequencies; these are 0.5 at both loci. (ii) The equilibrium frequency, $\hat{s}$, of Ab gametes; this is $\hat{s} = p_A q_B = 0.25$. (iii) The disequilibrium measure, D_0, in generation 0, before any recombination has taken place, and (iv) the disequilibrium, D_2, in generation 2. The disequilibrium in any generation, calculated from the Ab gamete frequencies, is $-D = s - \hat{s}$. In generation 0, $s = 0$ so $D_0 = \hat{s} = 0.25$. D_2 is got from [1.5]; the generation 2 progeny are the product of 2 generations of recombination, so $t = 2$ and $D_2 = D_0(1-c)^2$. With free recombination in question (1), $c = 0.5$ and $D_2 = 0.25(0.5)^2 = 0.0625$. With $c = 0.2$ in question (2), $D_2 = 0.25(0.8)^2 = 0.16$. Next we return to the equation $-D = s - \hat{s}$ given above. Writing this as $s = \hat{s} - D_2$ and substituting the values obtained for $\hat{s}$ and D_2 we get for generation 2,

(1) $s = 0.25 - 0.0625 = 0.1875$,   and   (2) $s = 0.25 - 0.16 = 0.09$.

Finally, the frequency of AA bb in the progeny produced by these gametes is s^2. The answers are therefore (1) 0.0352 and (2) 0.0081.

92 (2.9)   Let R be the resistance gene with frequency p, and S the susceptible allele; let s_1 be the selection coefficient against RR, given as $s_1 = 0.63$. To find the proportion of rats that die as a result of the poisoning we have to find s_2, the selection coefficient against SS. By [2.18]

$$\frac{s_2}{s_1} = \frac{p}{1-p}$$

$$s_2 = 0.63 \times \frac{0.34}{0.66} = 0.32$$

The proportion of deaths is

RR   SS
$s_1 p^2$ $+ s_2(1-p)^2$
$= 0.63(0.34)^2 + 0.32(0.66)^2$
$= 0.07$ $+ 0.14$
$= 0.21$

21 per cent of all rats die. This can be got more directly by [2.21] which gives the total deaths, i.e. the load, as

$$L = 0.63 \times 0.34 = 0.21.$$

93 (4.2) Substitute $N_m = N_f/d$ into [4.4] to give

$$\frac{1}{N_e} = \frac{d}{4N_f} + \frac{1}{4N_f} = \frac{d+1}{4N_f}$$

$$N_e = \frac{4N_f}{d+1}$$

94 (18.1) The required values of x and i are got from Appendix Table A, with interpolation. The correlations, t, are calculated from the approximate formula [18.1]. The values of r come from Table 9.3. The heritability is estimated by [18.2]. Taking first-degree relatives as an example,

$$t = (3.090 - 2.061)/3.367 = 0.306$$
$$h^2 = 2t = 0.61$$

	$p\%$	x	i	t	r	$h^2\%$
Population	0.1	3.090	3.367	—	—	—
Relatives						
1st degree	1.97	2.061	—	0.306	$\frac{1}{2}$	61
2nd degree	0.34	2.706	—	0.114	$\frac{1}{4}$	46
3rd degree	0.19	2.895	—	0.058	$\frac{1}{8}$	46

The estimate from first-degree relatives is likely to be the most precise, i.e. to have the smallest standard error, because the number of affected relatives is greatest and because the standard error of t is multiplied by 2 rather than by 4 or 8. On the other hand, first-degree relatives may have some environmental correlation through intra-uterine maternal effects. The most reliable estimate may perhaps be that from second-degree relatives. The fact that the third-degree relatives give an identical estimate may seem to support this view, but the standard errors are so large that little weight can be given to the identity of the two estimates. (A rough idea of the standard error of the correlation of relatives is given by

$$\sigma_t = \sqrt{\left[\frac{1}{i_r^4 A}\right]}$$

where i_r is the value of i corresponding to the incidence in the relatives and A is the observed number of affected relatives. By this approximate formula the standard errors of the three estimates of h^2 are 6, 11 and 28 per cent.)

95 (15.3) The first generation were full sibs, making $F = 0.25$. Assume that there was no further inbreeding and that non-additive genetic variance is negligible. Then rearranging [15.1] leads to

$$h_0^2 = \frac{h_t^2}{1 - F(1 - h_t^2)}$$

Substituting $h_t^2 = 0.34$ gives the heritability in the base population as

$$h_0^2 = \frac{0.34}{1-(0.25 \times 0.66)} = 0.41$$

96 (16.1) The predicted yield of a three-way cross is the mean of two single crosses. We therefore have to look for the best two single crosses in which three varieties are involved. The single-cross yields, in order of merit, are

Cross	AE	AC	BC	AB	DE	BE
Yield	31.8	22.8	16.5	14.1	13.1	12.4

The best two involve three varieties and so are suitable. The variety appearing in both would have to be used for the second cross, so the cross would be $(C \times E) \times A$, and its predicted yield is $\frac{1}{2}(AC + AE) = 27.3$.

The predicted yield of a four-way cross is the mean of four single crosses. We therefore have to look for the best four single crosses with four varieties each involved in two of the crosses. These are AE, AC, BC and BE. The cross would be made as $(A \times B) \times (C \times E)$, and its predicted yield is $\frac{1}{4}(AC + AE + BC + BE) = 20.9$.

97 (13.3) This index is dealt with on p. 221. The coefficients of the additive and the phenotypic components of the variance of observed family means in Table 13.3 are denoted by k and K respectively.

$$k = \frac{1 + (4 \times 0.5)}{5} = 0.600$$

$$K = \frac{1 + (4 \times 0.36)}{5} = 0.488$$

The weighting factors in the index are

$$b_1 = \frac{h^2(0.400)}{0.512}; \qquad b_2 = \frac{h^2(0.112)}{0.250}$$

and the index is

$$I = h^2(0.781)P_1 + h^2(0.448)P_2$$

where P_1 is the individual's gain and P_2 is the family mean, both being deviations from the population mean.

For convenience in application the index can be rescaled as

$$I' = P_1 + 0.574P_2$$

The rescaled index can also be calculated from [13.8].

Note that if the units of the index are to be units of weight gain, then P_2 in the rescaled index, and both P_1 and P_2 in the unscaled index, must be deviations from the population mean.

98 (10.6) We first have to calculate the observational components as shown in Table 10.3. Putting $d = 3$, $k = 10$, the mean squares of males are

$$3.894 = \sigma_W^2 + 10\sigma_D^2 + 30\sigma_S^2$$
$$2.198 = \sigma_W^2 + 10\sigma_D^2$$
$$1.125 = \sigma_W^2$$

From these equations, and the corresponding ones for females, the observational components and the correlations are as follows.

	Males	Females
Components		
Between sires, σ_S^2	0.05653	0.0800
Between dams, σ_D^2	0.1073	0.1168
Within dams, σ_W^2	1.125	0.893
Total σ_T^2	1.28883	1.0898
Correlations		
Half-sib, σ_S^2/σ_T^2	0.0439	0.0734
Full-sib, $(\sigma_S^2 + \sigma_D^2)/\sigma_T^2$	0.1271	0.1806

The relationship between observational and causal components is given in Table 10.4. The estimates of the causal components are as follows.

	Bristle units		Per cent of total	
	Males	Females	Males	Females
$V_A = 4\sigma_S^2$	0.2261	0.3200	17.5	29.4
$\frac{1}{4}V_D + V_{Ec} = \sigma_D^2 - \sigma_S^2$	0.0508	0.0368	3.9	3.4
$\frac{3}{4}V_D + V_{Ew} = \sigma_W^2 - 2\sigma_S^2$	1.0119	0.7330	78.5	67.3
$V_P = \sigma_T^2$	1.2888	1.0898	99.9	100.1

Without maternal half sibs V_{Ec} cannot be separated from $\frac{1}{4}V_D$, nor V_{Ew} from $\frac{3}{4}V_D$.

99 (14.4) The predicted depression is $0.56D_M + 0.64D_L$. Taking the values of D_M and D_L calculated in Problem 14.3 for the non-inbred mean of 8.3, this gives the depression as

$$(0.56 \times 4.2) + (0.64 \times 2.05) = 3.66$$

The means in Fig. 14.2(a), read from the graph, are approximately 7.6 at $F = 0$ and 4.2 at the last generation, giving a depression of 3.4 young per litter. This agrees very well with the prediction.

100 (19.7) Let subscripts 1 denote growth (G) and 2 denote food consumption (F). The index equations from [19.11] are

$$b_1 P_{11} + b_2 P_{12} = A_{11}$$
$$b_1 P_{21} + b_2 P_{22} = A_{21}$$

Substitute the given parameter estimates into [19.12]:

$$P_{11} = (1.11)^2 = 1.2321$$
$$P_{22} = (2.48)^2 = 6.1504$$
$$P_{12} = P_{21} = 0.83 \times 1.11 \times 2.48 = 2.2848$$
$$A_{11} = 0.52 \times (1.11)^2 = 0.6407$$
$$A_{21} = 0.71 \times \sqrt{(0.52 \times 0.40)} \times 1.11 \times 2.48 = 0.8914$$

Substitute these values into the index equations:

$$1.2321\, b_1 + 2.2848\, b_2 = 0.6407 \qquad\qquad (1)$$
$$2.2848\, b_1 + 6.1504\, b_2 = 0.8914 \qquad\qquad (2)$$

$(1) \times 6.1504$: $\quad 7.5779\, b_1 + 14.05\, b_2 = 3.9406$ $\qquad\qquad (3)$

$(2) \times 2.2848$: $\quad 5.2203\, b_1 + 14.05\, b_2 = 2.0367$ $\qquad\qquad (4)$

$(3) - (4)$: $\qquad\quad 2.3576\, b_1 \qquad\qquad\quad = 1.9039$

$$b_1 = 0.8076$$

Substitute b_1 into (1):

$$b_2 = -0.1551$$

The index is

$$I = 0.808G - 0.155F$$

Or, rescaled to give unit weight to G, in the form

$$I' = G + WF$$

where $W = b_2/b_1$, it is

$$I' = G - 0.192F$$

101 (1.11) The single-locus genotypes are now not in Hardy–Weinberg proportions in the generation 0 progeny, because the gene frequencies are different in the male and female parents. This affects the disequilibrium in generation 1 which must therefore be worked out first. Recombinant gametes are produced only by the AB/ab genotype. Here all the generation 0 progeny are of this genotype, so s_1 (the frequency of Ab gametes) is $\frac{1}{2}c$. (In Problem 1.10 only half of the generation 0 progeny were AB/ab, so s_1 was half as great.) The rest of the calculation is as follows.

	(1) $c = 0.5$	(2) $c = 0.2$
$s_1 = \frac{1}{2}c$	0.25	0.10
equilibrium, $\hat{s}$	0.25	0.25
$D_1 = \hat{s} - s_1$	0	0.15
$D_2 = D_1(1 - c)$, by [1.5],	0	0.12
$s_2 = \hat{s} - D_2$	0.25	0.13
s_2^2 (freq. of AA bb)	0.0625	0.0169

There is less disequilibrium following the 'cross' than after the 'mixture' of the strains in Problem 1.10. With no linkage the two-locus equilibrium frequencies are attained in generation 1, which corresponds with the F_2 of a classical two-factor cross with genotype frequencies of 1/16.

102 (2.10) Genotype frequencies among the parents (both genes) and gene frequency, q_0, of mutant:

AA	Aa	aa	q_0
0.6	0	0.4	0.4

Gene (a) gamete frequencies:

	A	a	Total
	0.6	0.4×0.5	0.8
Divided by 0.8:	0.75	0.25	1.0

Random union among these gametes gives the genotype frequencies in the progeny:

AA	Aa	aa
0.5625	0.3750	0.0625

The observed gene frequency in the progeny, by [1.1], is $q_1 = 0.25$. This is the same as in the gametes. Hardy–Weinberg expectations based on q_1 are therefore exactly as observed. The progeny alone give no evidence of selection.

Gene (b): gamete frequency of mutant is $q_0 = 0.4$. With random mating the genotype frequencies in the progeny are

	BB	Bb	bb	Total
in zygotes	0.36	0.48	0.16	1.00
in survivors	0.36	0.48	0.08	0.92
observed	0.391	0.522	0.087	1.000

Observed gene frequency by [1.1]: $q_1 = 0.348$, which gives Hardy–Weinberg expectations

$$0.425 \quad 0.454 \quad 0.121$$

The observed frequencies have an excess of heterozygotes and a deficiency of both homozygotes, suggesting to the unwary that selection favoured heterozygotes. The progeny alone tell us only that the conditions for Hardy–Weinberg expectations have not all been met. Δq is greater for gene (a) because there were no heterozygotes among the parents and all mutant genes were exposed to selection in homozygotes. With gene (b) many mutant genes were sheltered from selection in heterozygotes.

103 (4.3) Remember that 500 breeding pairs means $N = 1000$.

$N_e = 253$ by [4.6];
$\Delta F = 0.20$ per cent by [4.1].

104 (18.2) The required values of x and i from Appendix Table A are given below. The correlations, t, are calculated by [18.1]. The correlations are multiplied by 2 to give the heritability because $r = \frac{1}{2}$. The two estimates agree very well. The 'repeat births' are treated in the same way as relatives to give the correlation which is the repeatability. It is calculated as $(1.812 - 1.282)/2.208 = 0.24$.

	$p\%$	x	i	t	$h^2\%$
Population	3.5	1.812	2.208	—	—
Mothers	4.6	1.685	—	0.0575	12
Daughters	4.8	1.665	—	0.0666	13
Repeat births	10.0	1.282	—	0.24	—

105 (15.4)   One quarter of the mutations occurring will be fixed in a sib-mated line, in which there are 4 gametes per generation. So the number of mutations found is the mutation rate per gamete. The number of generations by which the sublines were separated is $21 + 29 = 50$, and there were 27 characters. Therefore the total mutation rate per gamete per generation per character is

$$\frac{5}{50 \times 27} = 3.7 \times 10^{-3}$$

This is the total mutation rate. If the mutation rate per locus is u and if each character can be affected by mutations at any of n loci, then

$$3.7 \times 10^{-3} = nu$$

We can take our choice as to what is the most credible combination of values for u and n, e.g.

u	n
3.7×10^{-3}	1
3.7×10^{-4}	10
3.7×10^{-5}	100

106 (16.2)   Let A, B, and AB represent the performances of the two lines or breeds and the single cross or F_1.

Generation	Genotypes crossed	Expected performance of progeny
1	AA $\times$ BB	AB
2	AB $\times$ AA	$(AB + A)/2$
3	AB $\Big\}$ $\times$ BB AA	$(3AB + B)/4$
4	3AB $\Big\}$ $\times$ AA BB	$(5AB + 3A)/8$

107 (13.4)   We use the rescaled index in which P_1 is the individual weight gain and P_2 is the family mean, which must be expressed as a deviation from the population mean; b_2 is the weighting factor for P_2. Problem 13.3 gave $b_2 = 0.574$ for families of $n=5$. For $n=8$, $k=0.5625$ and $K=0.4400$, giving $b_2 = 0.636$. The index values of the individuals are

A: $1.6 + (0.574 \times -0.2) = 1.485$
B: $1.5 + (0.574 \times 0.1) = 1.557$
C: $1.5 + (0.636 \times 0.1) = 1.564$
D: $1.3 + (0.636 \times 0.2) = 1.427$

The order of merit is C, B, A, D.

(*Note*: P_2 has to be a deviation from the population mean because its weighting (b_2) is not the same in all individuals. P_1 does not have to be a deviation because its weighting is the same. It is sensible to have an index whose mean is equal to the population mean or to zero. If all measurements in the index are expressed as deviations, then the index itself is a deviation and its mean is zero. If one measurement is in actual units, then all others must be deviations and the index then has a mean equal to the population mean.)

108   (10.7)   Consider first the particular case of $t=0.75$, $h^2 = 0.5$. Let $V_P = 100$. Then $V_A = 50$ and $cov_{FS} = 75$.

$$cov_{FS} = \tfrac{1}{2}V_A + \tfrac{1}{4}V_D + V_{Ec} = 75$$

Therefore

$$\tfrac{1}{4}V_D + V_{Ec} = 75 - 25 = 50$$

Now, the phenotypic variance can be written as

$$V_P = V_A + (\tfrac{1}{4}V_D + V_{Ec}) + \tfrac{3}{4}V_D + V_{Ew} = 100$$

Therefore

$$\tfrac{3}{4}V_D + V_{Ew} = 100 - 50 - 50 = 0$$

So h^2 cannot be greater than 0.5 because neither V_D nor V_{Ew} can be less than zero.

To generalize, consider the variance within full-sib families (see Table 10.4), which is

$$\tfrac{1}{2}V_A + \tfrac{3}{4}V_D + V_{Ew} = V_P - cov_{FS} = V_P(1-t)$$
$$\tfrac{1}{2}V_A = V_P(1-t) - \tfrac{3}{4}V_D - V_{Ew}$$

V_A is therefore maximal when V_D and V_{Ew} are zero. The value of h^2 at its maximum is thus

$$\tfrac{1}{2}h^2 = 1 - t$$
$$h^2 = 2(1-t)$$

If the full-sib correlation is 0.8, the maximum possible heritability is

$$h^2 = 2 \times 0.2 = 0.4$$

A character with $V_{Ew} = 0$ is extremely improbably, especially if V_{Ec} is not zero, so in practice the upper limit of h^2 will be substantially lower than $2(1-t)$.

109   (14.5)   We shall calculate the average selection differential on females required per generation. With $N_e = 40$ the rate of inbreeding, by [4.1] was $\Delta F = 0.0125$. The inbreeding coefficient at generation 30, by [3.12], was $F = 0.3143$. With slow inbreeding like this it is a good enough approximation to take the inbreeding coefficients of mothers and litters as being the same. The depression from mothers and litters together will be taken from the solution to Problem 14.3 as being 6.25 for $F = 1$. Therefore the expected depression at $F = 0.3143$ is $0.3143 \times 6.25 = 1.964$, and the rate per generation is $1.964/30 = 0.065$. Counteracting selection would be required to give a response of 0.065 per generation. Putting $h^2 = 0.22$ into [11.2], this makes $S = 0.065/0.22 = 0.30$. With no selection on males, the selection differential on females would have to be 0.6 mice per litter each generation on average. This means that if, for example, 1 in 5 females in each generation were replacements subject to selection, they would have had to come from litters averaging $0.6 \times 5 = 3$ mice per litter above their generation mean.

110   (19.8)   The predicted response to selection for the index is given by [19.17], but we first need to find the variance of index values by [19.18], for which we need the unscaled values $b_1 = 0.8076$ and $b_2 = -0.1551$. By [19.18]

$$\sigma_I^2 = b_1 A_{11} + b_2 A_{21}$$
$$= (0.8076 \times 0.6407) + (-0.1551 \times 0.8914)$$
$$= 0.3792$$
$$\sigma_I = 0.6158$$

The response to selection by the index, by [19.17], is

$$R_I = 1.5775 \times 0.6158$$
$$= 0.971$$

The units in which the index was calculated in Problem 19.7 were 100 g. Therefore the predicted improvement is 97 g per generation.

The response to selection for growth alone was calculated in Problem 19.3. In 100 g units it is $R = 0.911$. So the relative effectiveness of index selection is

$$\frac{R_I}{R} = \frac{0.971}{0.911} = 1.066$$

The index is expected to be 6.6 per cent better. In this case the use of the secondary character gives little benefit.

111   (11.7)   Both the intensity of selection and the generation length are now different for males and females. Assume that the numbers of males and females are equal at maturity. The average number of lambs per ewe per season is 1.2 as stated in Problem 11.6. The number of male lambs per male parent per season is therefore $\frac{1}{2} \times 1.2 \times 10 = 6$. The males are bred for 2 seasons, so each has on average 12 male offspring from which 1 must be selected, giving $i = 1.840$. The selection intensity on females for female replacements is $i = 0.704$ as calculated in Problem 11.6. The generation length is 2.5 years for males and 3 years for females. The mean intensity of selection per year is therefore

$$\frac{\frac{1}{2}(1.840+0.704)}{\frac{1}{2}(2.5+3)}=0.463$$

The effectiveness relative to the optimal procedure in Problem 11.6 is 0.463/0.274 = 1.69. It would be 69 per cent better.

The reason why there is an optimal age for discarding parents is that L increases by equal steps but i increases by diminishing steps. The reason for the optimal age being lower is the greater intensity of selection on males. The optimal age for discarding both sexes depends on the mean i and the mean L, not on the ratio of i to L in each sex separately.

112 (2.11) The effect of selection in males and females is different and has to be worked out separately. The heterogametic sex will be referred to as male. Let q be the initial frequency of the recessive lethal gene. The genotypes and their initial frequencies are shown below, with the gene frequencies among the survivors and in the next generation. For the gene frequency among surviving females see the derivation of [2.9].

	Males		Females		
	A	a	AA	Aa	aa
	p	q	p^2	$2pq$	q^2
Gene frequency					
in survivors	0		$q/(1+q)$		
in next generation	$q/(1+q)$		$\frac{1}{2}q/(1+q)$		

The overall gene frequency among survivors of both sexes is

$$q_1=\frac{2q}{3(1+q)}\qquad\text{(see [1.4]).}$$

In the zygotes of the next generation the gene frequency is no longer the same in the two sexes, but the overall gene frequency is not further changed. We can therefore take the above expression for q_1 as the overall gene frequency after one generation of selection. The change of gene frequency is then

$$\Delta q=\frac{2q}{3(1+q)}-q$$

which simplifies to

$$\Delta q=-\frac{q(1+3q)}{3(1+q)}$$

113 (4.4) The self-fertile variety breeds as an idealized population, for which $N_e=N$; $\Delta F=1/2N_e=2.50$ per cent. With the self-sterile variety $\Delta F=2.44$ per cent by [4.2b]. Exclusion of self-fertilization makes little difference, and even less with larger N.

114 (18.3)   This form of analysis is equivalent to working on the '0, 1' scale. It makes no difference if the values assigned to individuals are 0 and 1 rather than 1 and 2. Each half-sib family has a mean which, with values 0, 1, is the proportion of its members that have twins. The covariance of half sibs is thus the variance of the proportion among half-sib families. On the 0, 1 scale, then, the heritability is $4 \times 0.0058 = 2.32$ per cent. This can be converted to the liability scale by [18.4]. We need the population incidence and the corresponding i, which from Problem 18.2 are $p = 0.035$, $i = 2.208$. The heritability of liability is then

$$h^2 = \frac{2.32 \times 0.965}{(2.208)^2 \times 0.035} \text{ per cent} = 13 \text{ per cent}$$

which agrees very closely with the estimate obtained by the analysis of liability in Problem 18.2.

115 (15.5)   The component of variance between crosses, σ_X^2, comes directly from [15.4]. The total variance is the same as that of the base population, so the component within crosses, σ_W^2, is the difference from V_P. The component of variance between crosses, σ_X^2, is the variance of the true means of crosses. The variance of observed means, σ_M^2, is $\sigma_X^2 + \frac{1}{20}\sigma_W^2$. (See Table 13.3.)

		Between crosses	Within crosses	Observed means
	F	$FV_A + F^2V_D = \sigma_X^2$	$\sigma_W^2 = V_P - \sigma_X^2$	$\sigma_M^2 = \sigma_X^2 + \frac{1}{20}\sigma_W^2$
(1)	0.5	$432 + 47 = 479$	5319	745
(2)	1.0	$864 + 188 = 1052$	4746	1289

116 (16.3)   Let A, B, and C represent the purebred performances, and AB, AC, BC the single-cross performances.

Generation	Genotypes crossed	Expected performance of progeny
1	$AA \times BB$	AB
2	$AB \times CC$	$(AC + BC)/2$
2	$\left.\begin{array}{l} AC \\ BC \end{array}\right\} \times AA$	$(2AC + AB + A)/4$
4	$\left.\begin{array}{l} 2AC \\ AB \\ AA \end{array}\right\} \times BB$	$(5AB + 2BC + B)/8$
5	$\left.\begin{array}{l} 5AB \\ 2BC \\ BB \end{array}\right\} \times CC$	$(9BC + 5AC + 2C)/16.$

117 (13.5) For calculating the efficiency we need the coefficients of the un-scaled index. These were found in Problem 13.3 to be

$$b_1 = 0.781h^2; \qquad b_2 = 0.448h^2$$

It is not necessary to know h^2 because it will cancel out when the comparison with individual selection is made.

Next we need the variance of the index given by [13.12]. In this $A_{11} = \sigma_A^2$; A_{21}, the additive covariance of an individual with its family mean, is equal to the additive variance of observed family means, which is $k\sigma_A^2$. Substitution into [13.12] then gives

$$\sigma_I^2 = (b_1 + b_2 k)h^2 \sigma_A^2$$
$$= 1.050\, h^2 \sigma_A^2$$

The expected response to selection by the index is given by [13.15] as

$$R_I = i\sigma_I = i(1.025)h\sigma_A$$

This is directly comparable with the expected response to individual selection, R, in [11.4], and, provided the intensity of selection, i, is the same

$$R_I/R = 1.025$$

Index selection would be 2.5 per cent better than individual selection. The benefit is small because t is not very different from r.

118 (10.8) All three regressions and the full-sib correlation are significantly different from zero but, with the large standard errors, the partitioning of the variance can only be tentative. The regression of offspring on midparent estimates the heritability without bias from the assortative mating, giving $h^2 = 0.82$. Correcting the regressions on one parent for the bias caused the assortative mating ($r = 0.33$) by equation (14) of Table 10.6 gives $h^2 = 2b/(1+r)$ $= 0.71$ and 0.72 respectively. These are not inconsistent with the estimate from the midparent regression. To deal with the effect of assortative mating on the sib correlation we need to know the correlation of breeding values, m. Not knowing this, we might take $m = r$ as an approximation. Then the correlation of full sibs in respect of breeding values, from equation (15) of Table 10.6, and taking $h^2 = 0.82$, is $t = 0.41 \times 1.33 = 0.55$. The observed correlation is higher than this, though not significantly, suggesting that there may be some environmental variance common to full sibs, or some dominance variance, amounting to $0.71 - 0.55 = 16$ per cent of the total variance.

119 (14.6) Let $\overline{P}$ be the mean yield of the two parents and let F_1, F_2, F_3 represent the yields of these generations. Then the predicted yields are

$$F_2 = \tfrac{1}{2}(\overline{P} + F_1)$$
$$F_3 = \tfrac{1}{2}(\overline{P} + F_2)$$

giving

Cross	Observed		Predicted	
	$\bar{P}$	F_1	F_2	F_3
(1)	1.40	1.41	1.405	1.40
(2)	1.08	1.42	1.25	1.165

The reasons for these expectations may be made clearer by consideration of the heterosis, H. By definition, $H_{F_1} = F_1 - \bar{P}$. By [14.10]*, $H_{F_2} = \frac{1}{2}H_{F_1}$. The expected yield of the F_2 is

$$\bar{P} + H_{F_2} = \bar{P} + \frac{1}{2}(F_1 - \bar{P}) = \frac{1}{2}(\bar{P} + F_1).$$

Each generation of selfing halves the frequency of heterozygotes (Table 5.1), so the expected heterosis in the F_3 is half that of the F_2. Thus the predicted yield of the F_3 is $\bar{P} + \frac{1}{2}(F_2 - \bar{P}) = \frac{1}{2}(\bar{P} + F_2)$.

* By an error the $\frac{1}{2}$ is omitted from this equation in the first printing of the 2nd edition.

120 (19.9)   The correlated response is given by [19.19], but we first need to get the additive genetic covariance of character 2 with the index. The covariance of character 1 with the index is given by [19.20]. The covariance of character 2 with the index, which is given in Example 19.4, is

$$cov_{2I} = b_2 A_{22} + b_1 A_{21}$$

A_{22} was not calculated in Problem 19.7. It is $0.40 \times (2.48)^2 = 2.4602$.

$$cov_{2I} = (-0.1551 \times 2.4602) + (0.8076 \times 0.8914)$$
$$= 0.3383$$

To get the response from [19.19] we need $i = 1.5775$ and $\sigma_I = 0.6158$, both coming from Problem 19.8. The correlated response of food consumption is then

$$CR_2 = 1.5775 \times \frac{0.3383}{0.6158}$$
$$= 0.87 \text{ (in 100 g units)}$$

The food consumption would be expected to increase by 87 g per generation.

121 (11.8)   Let n be the number of litters on which selection is based, and let t be the generation length in years. Let R and R_n be the responses when selection is based on 1 and on n litters respectively. The responses can be compared by [11.3], $R = ih^2\sigma_P$, but it is simpler to do so by [11.4], $R = ih\sigma_A$, because σ_A does not change with the number of litters. We do not need to evaluate the actual responses because the optimal value of n will be the number that gives the maximal value of the ratio

$$\frac{R_n/t_n}{R/t} = \frac{i_n}{i}\frac{h_n}{h}\frac{t}{t_n}$$

The calculations are shown below. Note that the expected number of females in each litter is 4, so the proportion of sows that must be selected is 1/4 with $n=1$, 1/8 with $n=2$ etc. The ratio h_n^2/h^2 was calculated in Problem 8.6 for the repeatability of 0.409. The values of i are found from Appendix Table A.

n	t	$p\%$	i	h_n^2/h^2	i_n/i	h_n/h	t/t_n	$\dfrac{R_n/t_n}{R/t}$
1	1	25	1.271	—	—	—	—	—
2	1.5	12.5	1.647	1.42	1.296	1.192	0.667	1.03
3	2	8.33	1.840	1.65	1.448	1.285	0.500	0.93

The optimal number of litters is 2.

122 (2.12) Assume that the gene frequency will be low enough for females homozygous for the deleterious gene to be ignored, as an approximation. Elimination of the gene by selection then takes place only in males. One third of the genes are in males, so the proportion $sq/3$ of the genes are eliminated by selection in each generation, where s is the coefficient of selection. At equilibrium these are replaced by mutation, so $sq/3=u$, and $q=3u/s$.

The muscular dystrophy data fit this expectation very well with $s=1$ and no selection against heterozygous females. The gene frequency, neglecting the male–female difference, is the incidence in males, which is almost exactly three times the estimated mutation rate, as expected.

123 (4.5) Let $k=$number of offspring used, i.e. family size, as given. The actual number of parents, including the sterile pair, is $N=16$. To get N_e from [4.7] we need to calculate the variance of k. The mean is $\bar{k}=2$, and the deviations $(k-\bar{k})$ are: -2, -1, -1, 0, 0, $+1$, $+1$, $+2$, from which $\Sigma(k-\bar{k})^2=12$ and $V_k=12/8=1.5$. (Divided by 8, not 7, because this is the whole 'population' in the statistical sense, not a sample.) Then by [4.7] $N_e=64/3.5=18.3$. N_e is still a little larger than N in spite of the failure to equalize family size.

124 (18.4) Care is needed with the signs of x and i. Here x will denote the population mean as a deviation from the threshold so that, with incidences less than 50 per cent, x is negative. The mean of affected individuals, i_A, is a deviation from the population mean and is positive. We shall need also the mean of unaffected individuals, i_N, and this is negative. Appendix Table A provides values of i_A for the incidence, p, and $i_N=-i_A p/(1-p)$, as stated on p. 279. The two generations have to be worked out separately because the change of incidence resulting from the first selection changes the selection differential in the second selection.

Selection for reduced incidence will be explained first because it is simpler. The working is shown below. Since more than 50 per cent of individuals are normal all selected individuals of both sexes will be normal and the selection differential in standard deviation units will be $S=i_N$. The response is $R=h^2S$, and the new mean liability is $x_1=x_0+R$. To get the new incidence we have to find the value of p corresponding to x_1 in Appendix Table A. The values given were obtained by interpolation, but it will make little difference if the nearest tabulated value of p is taken. For the second generation the calculation is repeated using p_1 and x_1 in place of p_0 and x_0. The prediction is that the incidence will be reduced to 17 per cent.

Selection for reduced incidence

First selection		Second selection	
p_0	23%	p_1	19.6%
x_0	−0.739	x_1	−0.857
i_A	1.320	i_A	1.411
$S = i_N$	−0.394	$S = i_N$	−0.344
$R = 0.3S$	−0.118	$R = 0.3S$	−0.103
$x_1 = x_0 + R$	−0.857	$x_2 = x_1 + R$	−0.960
p_1	19.6%	p_2	16.9%

The calculation of selection for increased incidence, shown below, is the same as before except that the selection differential is more complicated. Since the proportion of selected males is less than the incidence, all selected males will be affected and the selection differential on males will be $S_\delta = i_A$. The selected females, however, will have to include some normals because fewer than 50 per cent are affected. In the first selection, the proportion of the selected females that are affected will be $0.23/0.5 = 0.46$, and the proportion that are normal will be 0.54. The selection differential on females will thus be $S_\female = 0.46i_A + 0.54i_N$. Or, in terms of the incidence, $S_\female = 2pi_A + (1 - 2p)i_N$. The combined selection on both sexes will be $\frac{1}{2}(S_\female + S_\delta)$. The rest of the calculation needs no further explanation. After the second selection the incidence will be increased to 41 per cent. The much greater response to selection for increased incidence results from the larger selection differential.

Selection for increased incidence

First selection		Second selection	
p_0	23%	p_1	31.5%
x_0	−0.739	x_1	−0.482
i_A	1.320	i_A	1.128
i_N	−0.394	i_N	−0.519
$S_\delta = i_A$	1.320	S_δ	1.128
$S_\female = 2pi_A + (1 - 2p)i_N$	0.3944	$S_\female$	0.5186
$S = \frac{1}{2}(S_\female + S_\delta)$	0.8572	S	0.8233
$R = 0.3S$	0.257	R	0.247
x_1	−0.482	x_2	−0.235
p_1	31.5%	p_2	40.7%

125 (15.6) Let X be the true mean and M the observed mean of a cross. Selecting 1 out of 50 gives $i = 2.249$ from Appendix Table B. The deviation of the best cross from the mean of all the crosses is therefore $i\sigma_M$, where σ_M is the standard deviation of observed means. σ_M^2 was calculated in Problem 15.5. The expected mean of all crosses is the original population mean, which was 308. Adding 308 to $i\sigma_M$ gives the predicted observed mean of the best cross.

	F	σ_X^2	σ_M^2	σ_M	$i\sigma_M$	M, predicted
(1)	0.5	479	745	27.3	61.4	369.4
(2)	1.0	1052	1289	35.9	80.7	388.7

The prediction of future performance was explained in Chapter 8 in connection with repeatability. The expected mean of the repeated cross, the future performance, is the true mean of the cross. To predict the true mean we need to know the regression of true means on observed means. The observed mean is $M = X + E$, where E is the deviation due to sampling error. Now,

$$cov_{XM} = cov_{X.(X+E)} = cov_{XX} + cov_{XE}.$$

$cov_{XX} = \sigma_X^2$ and $cov_{XE} = 0$ because X and E are uncorrelated. Thus $cov_{XM} = \sigma_X^2$. The required regression is $b_{XM} = cov_{XM}/\sigma_M^2 = \sigma_X^2/\sigma_M^2$. The rest of the calculation is as follows.

	$b_{XM} = \sigma_X^2/\sigma_M^2$	Predicted true mean of best cross
(1)	0.643	$308 + 0.643(61.4) = 347.5$
(2)	0.816	$308 + 0.816(80.7) = 373.9$

126 (16.4) In each case the right-hand column of the table in the solution represents the proportion of each genotype in the progeny. It is simplest to consider the proportion of homozygotes, which is the inbreeding coefficient, F, relative to the first generation, in which there are no homozygotes. Then the amount of heterosis relative to that of the single crosses is $H_t = 1 - F_t$.

Generation	Two lines		Three lines	
(t)	F_t	H_t	F_t	H_t
1	0	1	0	1
2	1/2	0.5	0	1
3	1/4	0.75	1/4	0.75
4	3/8	0.625	1/8	0.875
5	(5/16)	0.6875	2/16	0.875
Many	1/3	0.667	1/7	0.857

If the series of generations were continued the heterosis would be found to settle down after a few cycles to 2/3 in the case of two lines and 6/7 in the case of three lines. The general formula for the final level of inbreeding relative to the first cross is $1/(2^n - 1)$, where n is the number of lines.

127   (13.6)   This is like the index on pp. 220–1 except that there is now more than one half sister. The index equations are

$$b_2 P_{22} + b_3 P_{23} = A_{21}$$
$$b_2 P_{32} + b_3 P_{33} = A_{31}$$

Subscript 1 refers to the individual to be selected, which is not measured; 2 refers to the mother and 3 refers to the mean of the half sisters. $P_{22} = \sigma^2$ (i.e. the phenotypic variance); $P_{23} = P_{32} = 0$; $P_{33} = K\sigma^2$, where $K = [1 + (n-1)t]/n$, as before. A_{21} is the additive covariance of the individual with its mother $= r_2 \sigma_A^2 = r_2 h^2 \sigma^2$, where $r_2 = \frac{1}{2}$. A_{31} is the additive covariance of the individual with the mean of its half sisters in which the individual is not included; this is the covariance relevant to sib selection (see p. 213) and is not affected by the number of half sibs, for the reason explained in the paragraph following equation [9.2]. Thus $A_{31} = r_3 h^2 \sigma^2$, where $r_3 = \frac{1}{4}$. Substituting these values in the index equations gives

$$b_2 \sigma^2 + 0 \qquad = r_2 h^2 \sigma^2$$
$$0 \quad + b_3 K \sigma^2 = r_3 h^2 \sigma^2$$

from which

$$b_2 = r_2 h^2 \quad = \tfrac{1}{2} h^2$$
$$b_3 = r_3 h^2 / K = \tfrac{1}{4} h^2 / K$$

Now evaluate K. Because there is no environmental resemblance between half sisters, $t = \tfrac{1}{4} h^2 = 0.0875$. With $n = 10$ this gives

$$K = \frac{1 + (9 \times 0.0875)}{10} = 0.17875$$

Substituting for K and for $h^2 = 0.35$ gives the unscaled index

$$I = 0.175 P_2 + 0.490 P_3$$

128   (10.9)   The equations in Table 10.6 provide the solutions. Because the choice of mates is purely phenotypic, $m = rh^2$. Then equation (15) is $t = \tfrac{1}{2} h^2 (1 + rh^2)$, where h^2 is the heritability in the population mating assortatively. Rearranging gives $\tfrac{1}{2} rh^4 + \tfrac{1}{2} h^2 - t = 0$, which has the solution

$$h^2 = [-\tfrac{1}{2} \pm \sqrt{(\tfrac{1}{4} + 2rt)}]/r.$$

Substituting the values of r and t gives only one possible solution, which is $h^2 = 0.50$. The heritability in the same population if it mated at random, h_0^2, is given by equation (9). Substituting $h^2 = 0.5$ and $m = rh^2 = 0.2$ gives

$$h_0^2 = 0.5 \ (0.8/0.9) = 0.44.$$

129   (14.7)   It follows from [14.10] that the difference between the F_1 and the F_2 is half the heterosis, i.e. $F_1 - F_2 = \tfrac{1}{2} H$, from which $H = -0.24$. But the difference between the F_1 and F_2 was very small and non-significant, so this small amount of heterosis deduced is not significantly different from zero. In fact the means of the parental varieties were 17.88 ± 0.24 and 15.00 ± 0.19, making $\bar{P} = 16.44 \pm 0.20$, and the observed heterosis was $H = -0.72 \pm 0.28$.

130   (19.10)   The index equations from [19.15] are

$$b_1 P_{11} + b_2 P_{12} = a_1 A_{11} + a_2 A_{12}$$
$$b_1 P_{21} + b_2 P_{22} = a_1 A_{21} + a_2 A_{22}$$

The left-hand sides, being phenotypic parameters, are the same as in Problem 19.7. For the right-hand sides we need $A_{11} = 0.6407$ and $A_{12} = A_{21} = 0.8914$, both also from Problem 19.7. $A_{22} = 2.4602$ as calculated in Problem 19.9. The economic values are already in the 100 g units used for the other parameters in the equations, so $a_1 = 8$ and $a_2 = -2$. The index equations with the values entered are

$$1.2321\, b_1 + 2.2848\, b_2 = (8 \times 0.6407) + (-2 \times 0.8914) = 3.3428$$
$$2.2848\, b_1 + 6.1504\, b_2 = (8 \times 0.8914) + (-2 \times 2.4602) = 2.2108$$

Eliminating b_2 as in Problem 19.7 gives

$$2.3576\, b_1 = 20.5596 - 5.0512$$
$$b_1 = 6.578$$
$$b_2 = -2.084$$

The index for selection is

$$I = 6.578G - 2.084F$$

or, more conveniently,

$$I' = G - 0.317F$$

131   (11.9)   We have first to get the coefficient of selection, s, acting on the gene by [11.8]. Substituting $2a = 0.3$, $\sigma_P = 2.0$ and $i = 1.755$ gives $s = 0.2633$. The gene frequency after one generation of selection is then given by line (1) of Table 2.2. The gene frequency q in the formula is that of the allele selected against, so we must put $q = 0.6$. The formula can be rewritten in a form that makes the substitutions simpler:

$$q_1 = q[1 - \tfrac{1}{2}s(1 + q)]/(1 - sq)$$
$$= 0.6[1 - 0.1316(1.6)]/(1 - 0.1580)$$
$$= 0.5625$$

For the second generation, put q_1 in place of q, giving

$$q_2 = 0.5245$$

The frequency of the increasing allele will therefore be 0.4755.

132   (2.13)   Initial gene frequency of red, $q_0 = \sqrt{(0.01)} = 0.10$. (1) By [2.9], $q_2 = 0.1/1.2 = 0.0833$. Frequency of red calves $= q_2^2 = 0.0069$. (2) This is tricky because more selection is applied to bulls than to cows. Consequently, after selection the gene frequency is not the same in the male and female parents and the genotypes in the progeny are not in Hardy–Weinberg frequencies. The change of gene frequency has to be worked out separately for each sex. The frequency of heterozygotes before selection is 0.18. The proportion of heterozygous bulls that will escape detection by having no red progeny in the test is

$(\frac{3}{4})^6 = 0.178$. The proportion of all bulls that are undetected heterozygotes is therefore $0.18 \times 0.178 = 0.0320$.

First generation	Bulls				Cows			
	RR	Rr	rr	Total	RR	Rr	rr	Total
Before selection	0.81	0.18	0.01	1.00	0.81	0.18	0.01	1.00
After selection	0.81	0.0320	0	0.8420	0.81	0.18	0	0.99
	0.9620	0.0380	0	1.0000	0.8182	0.1818	0	1.0000

$$q_{1m} = \tfrac{1}{2} \times 0.0380 = 0.0190 \qquad q_{1f} = \tfrac{1}{2} \times 0.1818 = 0.0909$$

Now make a table of gamete frequencies, like Table 1.2, and get the genotype frequencies in the progeny.

			Male gametes	
			R	r
			0.9810	0.0190
Female gametes	R	0.9091	0.8918	0.0173
	r	0.0909	0.0892	0.0017

Second generation	Bulls				Cows			
	RR	Rr	rr	Total	RR	Rr	rr	Total
Before selection	0.8918	0.1065	0.0017	1.0000	0.8918	0.1065	0.0017	1.0000
After selection	0.8918	0.0190	0	0.9108	0.8918	0.1065	0	0.9983
	0.9792	0.0208	0	1.0000	0.8933	0.1067	0	1.0000

$$q_{2m} = 0.0104 \qquad q_{2f} = 0.05335$$

The frequency of red calves in the progeny is $q_{2m}q_{2f} = 0.06$ per cent.

(Note: q_{1f} can be got more easily by [2.9], but q_{2f} cannot be got this way because the genotypes before the second selection are not in Hardy–Weinberg frequencies.)

133 (4.6) The breeding plan was minimal inbreeding with $N = 16$, so by [4.9], $N_e = 31$.

The data led to the inbreeding coefficient at generation 27 being $F(t = 27) = 0.447$. By [3.12]

$$
\begin{aligned}
(1 - \Delta F)^{27} &= 1 - 0.447 = 0.553 \\
27 \log (1 - \Delta F) &= -0.2573 \\
1 - \Delta F &= 0.9783 \\
\Delta F &= 0.0217 \\
N_e &= 1/(2\,\Delta F) = 23.0
\end{aligned}
$$

134 (18.5) Here x is the deviation of the threshold from the population mean. The values of x and i needed are as follows.

Class	$p\%$	x	i
N	20	-0.842	-1.400
$H+F$	80	-0.842	$+1.400 \times 20/80 = +0.350$
F	30	$+0.524$	$+1.159$

The value of i for $p=80$ per cent is the value for $p=20$ per cent multiplied by $(1-p)/p$, as stated at the head of Appendix Table A.

(1) Difference between thresholds
$$= 0.524 - (-0.842) = 1.366\sigma$$
1 t.u. $= 1.366\sigma$; $\sigma = 0.732$ t.u.

(2) Population mean as deviation from lower threshold
$$= +0.842\sigma = (0.842 \times 0.732) \text{ t.u.} = +0.616 \text{ t.u.}$$

(3) $\bar{N} = -1.400\sigma = -1.025$ t.u.
$\bar{F} = +1.159\sigma = +0.848$ t.u.
$(\overline{H+F}) = +0.350\sigma = +0.256$ t.u.

$(\overline{H+F})$ is the mean of all individuals above the lower threshold, made up of $50/80$ H and $30/80$ F. Therefore

$$(\overline{H+F}) = \frac{50}{80}\bar{H} + \frac{30}{80}\bar{F}$$
$$0.256 = 0.625\,\bar{H} + (0.375 \times 0.848)$$
$$\bar{H} = -0.099 \text{ t.u.}$$

To check, see that the mean of N, H, and F, each weighted by its frequency, sums to zero as the mean deviation from the population mean.

N: $-1.025 \times 0.2 = -0.2050$
H: $-0.099 \times 0.5 = -0.0495$
F: $+0.848 \times 0.3 = +0.2544$
$\qquad\qquad \Sigma = \overline{0.000}$

135 (15.7) The working follows exactly that of Example 15.2 and will not be explained in detail. The varieties themselves, whose yields are on the diagonal of the table, must be excluded because combining ability refers to performance in crosses. The values of T and G are on the right of the table below. G is the general combining ability of the variety indicated on the left of the table. As examples,

$$T_B = 14.1 + 16.5 + 6.2 + 12.4 = 49.2$$
$$G_B = \frac{49.2}{3} - \frac{302.6}{5 \times 3} = -3.77$$

The G's are deviations from the mean; to check, see that $\Sigma G = 0$.

The expected value of, for example, the cross $A \times B$ is

$$\overline{X} + G_A + G_B$$
$$= 15.13 + 8.36 - 3.77$$
$$= 19.72$$

The deviation (SCA + error) is therefore $14.1 - 19.72 = -5.62$. To check, see that the deviations sum to zero. The deviations are given in the table below.

	B	C	D	E	T	G
A	−5.62	+0.55	−1.25	+6.32	85.6	+8.36
B	—	+6.38	+0.18	−0.95	49.2	−3.77
C	—	—	−0.25	−6.68	56.8	−1.24
D	—	—	—	+1.32	44.5	−5.34
E	—	—	—	—	66.5	+1.99
Σ	—	—	—	—	302.6	0.00

$\overline{X} = 302.6/20 = 15.13$

136 (16.5) To avoid confusion, designate the breeds by letters to correspond with those used in Problem 16.3, as shown below. In calculating the expectations for each generation, remember that the formula for any generation applies to W in that generation and to N in the next. The required total litter weight is $W \times N$.

Breed or cross Designation	Y A	C B	D C	YC AB	YD AC	CD BC
W	84	78	88	90	96	92
N	7.9	6.6	6.3	8.2	7.3	7.4

Generation	Genotypes		Expectations		
	W	N	W	N	$W \times N$
1	AB	A	90	7.9	711
2	$X_1 \times C$	AB	94	8.2	771
3	$X_2 \times A$	$X_1 \times C$	91.5	7.35	673
4	$X_3 \times B$	$X_2 \times A$	89	7.675	683
5	$X_4 \times C$	$X_3 \times B$	92.75	7.8	723

Note that the crossbred performance fluctuates and none is better than the three-way cross in generation 2.

137 (13.7) The two intensities of selection cannot be combined because the standard deviation of the index is not the same as that of yield. The response has to be got from the predicted breeding values of males and of females. First, from [13.12]

$$\sigma_I^2 = b_2 A_{21} + b_3 A_{31}$$
$$= b_2 r_2 h^2 \sigma^2 + b_3 r_3 h^2 \sigma^2$$
$$= (b_2 r_2 + b_3 r_3) h^2 \sigma^2$$
$$= [(0.175 \times 0.5) + (0.490 \times 0.25)] \times 0.35 \times \sigma^2$$
$$= 0.0735 \, \sigma^2$$
$$\sigma_I = 0.2711 \times 696$$
$$= 188.69$$

Selecting 5 per cent of bulls gives $i = 2.063$, from Appendix Table A. The expected breeding value of the selected bulls is given by [13.15]:

Bulls' breeding value $= i\sigma_I = 2.063 \times 188.69 = 389.3$

Selecting 50 per cent of cows gives $i = 0.798$, and the predicted breeding value is given by [11.3] as:

Cows' breeding value $= ih^2 \sigma_P = 0.798 \times 0.35 \times 696 = 194.4$

Both breeding values are deviations from the population mean and the expected response is the mean of the two:

$$R = \tfrac{1}{2}(389.3 + 194.4)$$
$$= 292 \text{ kg.}$$

138   (10.10)   In all cases we need to know both N, the number of families, and n, the number of offspring or of sibs per family. The one of these that is not given has to be deduced from $T = 400$. The relationships of N and n to T are as follows.

(1) $T = N(n+1)$. $N = 200$, $n = 1$.
(2) $T = N(n+2)$. $n = 3$, $N = 80$.
(3) $T = Nn$. $n = 5$, $N = 80$.
(4) $T = Nn$. $N = 20$, $n = 20$.

In the case of (1) and (2) the number of individuals measured per family is the number of offspring, n, plus one parent in (1) and two parents in (2).

Equation [10.8] gives the sampling variance of the regression in (1) and (2), and [10.12] gives the sampling variance of the correlation in (3) and (4). In cases (1) and (4), however, the designs are optimal and there is a shorter way of getting the standard error of the heritability.

(1) The design is optimal because $n = 1$. With one parent measured ($k = 1$), [10.8] reduces to the s.e. of h^2 given in [10.9].

$\text{s.e.}(h^2) = 2/\sqrt{200} = 0.14$

(2) $k = 2$; $t = \tfrac{1}{2}h^2 = 0.3$ (neglecting dominance); $N = 80$; $n = 3$.

$$\sigma_b^2 = \frac{2[1 + (2 \times 0.3)]}{3 \times 80} = 0.0133$$
$$\sigma_b = 0.115$$

The heritability is estimated by b, so

$\text{s.e.}(h^2) = \sigma_b = 0.115$

(*Note*: The approximation here is not very good. The exact formula at the top of p. 166 gives $\sigma_b^2 = 0.0091$; s.e.$(h^2) = 0.095$.)

(3) $t = \frac{1}{2}h^2 = 0.2$ (neglecting dominance); $N = 80$; $n = 5$.

$$\sigma_t^2 = \frac{2[1 + (4 \times 0.2)]^2 (0.8)^2}{5 \times 4 \times 79} = 0.00262$$

$$\sigma_t = 0.051$$

h^2 is estimated as $2t$, so

$$\text{s.e.}(h^2) = 2\sigma_t = 0.10$$

(4) $N = 20$; $n = 20$.

This is the optimal design for half sibs because $n = 4/h^2$, and the sampling variance of the heritability is given approximately by [10.15].

$$\sigma_{h^2}^2 = (32 \times 0.2)/400 = 0.0160$$
$$\text{s.e.}(h^2) = 0.13$$

The exact formula, [10.12], gives s.e.$(h^2) = 0.12$.

139 (20.3) All that is needed before plotting the graph is to convert mortality to survival and, perhaps, to express birth weights as deviations from the mean in standard deviation units. For example

Birth weight, kg	Deviation in σ	Survival, %
1.3	−4.24	38.8
1.8	−3.25	66.7
etc.		

Note the flat-topped nature of the curve: 97 per cent of babies have survival probabilities within the narrow range of 97 to 99 per cent. The data give no grounds for believing that small babies die because they are small; they may be small because they have some other disability from which they die.

140 (19.11) The calculation follows that of Problem 19.8. The variance of the index, by [9.18], is

$$\sigma_I^2 = (6.578 \times 3.3428) + (-2.084 \times 2.2108) = 17.3816$$
$$\sigma_I = 4.169$$

The intensity of selection was found in Problem 19.3 to be $i = 1.5775$. Therefore the expected response to selection for the index is

$$R_I = 1.5775 \times 4.169$$
$$= 6.58$$

The predicted improvement in economic value is 6.58 cents per bird per generation.

When selection is made for growth alone, growth will increase as a direct response, giving an economic gain, and food consumption will increase as a correlated response, giving an economic loss. The responses were calculated in Problem 19.3. Converted to 100 g units the direct response of growth is $+0.911$ and the correlated response of food consumption is $+1.268$. The economic gain is therefore

From growth:	0.911×8	$=$ 7.29 cents
From food consumption:	$1.268 \times (-2) =$	-2.54 cents
Net economic gain		4.75 cents

The relative effectiveness of the index for improving economic value is thus $6.58/4.75 = 1.39$. The index would be 39 per cent better.